Analysis of Production Decline Curves

Analysis of Production Decline Curves

Steven W. Poston
Texas A&M University (retired)

Bobby D. Poe Jr.
Schlumberger

Society of Petroleum Engineers

ISBN 978-1-55563-144-4

08 09 10 11 12 13 14 15 / 9 8 7 6 5 4 3 2 1

Society of Petroleum Engineers
222 Palisades Creek Drive
Richardson, TX 75080-2040 USA

http://store.spe.org/
service@spe.org
1.972.952.9393

Preface

Decline curves are probably the most widely used and least understood production-forecasting technique currently in use in the industry. Analysis of decline curves provides an unsophisticated reservoir-evaluation tool, but profound economic decisions often rest on the outcome of the prediction. A simplistic view of decline-curve analysis can lead to wide misuse, often caused by misunderstandings.

There has been no single reference book on the meaning of production decline curves, their application, and their use and misuse. We have endeavored to provide such a reference. Early on, engineers recognized the characteristic decline of oil- and gas-well performance and attempted to provide some mathematical sense of the performance data by fitting equations of lines to the production history.

Arps, of course, was the first to gather most of the often disparate material to develop an empirical analysis theory for estimating future rate-time and expected recovery behavior. The upshot of applying the Arps equations during the "slide rule days" was that an exponential decline curve could be analyzed in a straightforward manner. On the other hand, the equations for the harmonic and hyperbolic curves could be determined only by laborious trial-and-error methods. The technology pretty much stayed "as is" until the advent of the personal computer, when statistical trial-and-error routines and the Arps equations could be combined to provide a nearly instantaneous and widely used analysis tool. All these principles have been developed in Chapter 1, "Introduction to Decline Curves," while Chapter 2, "Application of Decline Curves," delves into the application of decline-analysis techniques to actual field conditions.

In the mid-1970s, Cox showed that the empirical exponential decline was observed in the solution of the diffusivity equation for a semicompressible fluid producing under pseudosteady-state flow conditions, and he applied these findings to solving field problems.

Chapter 3, "Type Curves," discusses how Fetkovich applied a cohesive set of type curves to facilitate analysis of a wide range of well performance data. These decline curves covered both transient and boundary-dominated reservoir flow conditions and were extremely easy to use, although some of the equations are cumbersome.

The discussion in Chapter 4, "The Exponential Decline Curve," illuminates the difference between the constant percentage and continuous decline rate solutions, as well as the uses for the rate-cumulative recovery plot. An exponential decline usually indicates production of a semicompressible fluid from a homogeneous reservoir. Divergence from the straightline logarithmic rate-time plot indicates that reservoir abnormalities are influencing the well performance history. Changing compressibility and viscosity and the effects of layering and commingling are some of the more prevalent causes for this divergence. Chapter 5, "The Hyperbolic Decline Curve," and Chapter 6, "Interpretation of Field Curves," discuss the effects of these variables on the shape of the decline curve. Of particular importance in Chapter 6 is the practical coupling of known field-decline averages with well performance curves exhibiting b equal to or greater than 1. This, of course, is a theoretical and practical impossibility, but some accommodation must be reached to arrive at a reasonable well performance prediction.

Chapter 7, "Production Performance Plots," develops the simplistic but practical application of the oil/water ratio (OWR) and gas/oil ratio (GOR) curves to interpret reservoir performance. Equating these plots to field geology and knowledge of operational history provides a straightforward analysis method.

Many of the pressure- and rate-transient analysis methods used earlier in well-testing practice have more recently been employed in the evaluation of the production performance of oil and gas wells. Chapter 8, "Recent Developments in Decline-Curve Analyses," provides a summary of the state-of-the-art production decline-curve-analysis techniques available in the industry today. Many of the modern production decline-curve-analysis software models currently available commercially use the well performance analysis and evaluation principles presented in Chapter 8. Recent advances in decline-curve analysis that have aided in improved well production performance analysis are the introduction of the integral and integral-derivative decline analysis plotting functions, as well as the use of an equivalent time-scaling function that can be evaluated from the production performance.

It is the hope of the authors that this book may serve as a solid reference on which further development in production decline-curve analyses, interpretation, and innovative production diagnostic evaluation methodologies are based. Production decline-curve analyses have a long and storied history, but that history is far from over. There is always room in this industry for truly innovative and useful production performance analyses and technologies.

Acknowledgments

In writing this book, there have been a number of "helpers" who contributed along the way.

R.L. Whiting provided encouragement in many ways that he did not realize, while D. Von Gonten provided the first author with the opportunity to leave the industry and return to a very good petroleum engineering department at Texas A&M University, where he was able to coalesce his technical and industry experiences to provide practical methods to solve some of the oilfield problems encountered in practice.

Of paramount importance has been the assistance of Raj Raghavan, who urged the first author of this book to construct this book and has, over the course of its development, provided exhaustive comments and advice on the theme of the book and its technical content. The authors will always be indebted to him.

The patient and diligent editing of the manuscript by Stuart Filler is also greatly appreciated. His efforts helped make a collection of (at times) disorganized text understandable and consistent, and he provided many useful, practical, and constructive comments for the book.

Finally, the authors are indebted to SPE for the support and interest demonstrated for the subject of this text, and in permitting the authors of this book the opportunity to address many of the recent advances in the current technology of decline-curve analysis. After all these years, that technology is still evolving.

Steven Poston
Bobby D. Poe Jr.

Contents

Chapter 1

Introduction to Decline Curves

Oil and gas production rates from a well or property generally decline as a function of time. Loss of reservoir pressure or changing produced-fluid ratios are the chief culprits for the decline. Fitting a line through the declining production values and assuming this same line trends similarly into the future forms the basis for the decline-curve analysis method.

Decline-curve analysis is widely applied for evaluating the potential of a producing property in a case in which information is sparse. The absence of sufficient log, core, and fluid analysis, static bottomhole pressure surveys, and well-test data precludes application of more advanced analysis techniques. Therefore, a Hobson's choice is usually exercised, and production decline curves are examined to forecast the remaining potential of economically marginal properties.

However, other analysis methods may also be applied to study producing properties. The following discussion compares the major characteristics of four broad groups of predictive models to acquaint the reader to the role of decline-curve analysis in the hierarchy of reservoir evaluation techniques.

1.1 Comparing Predictive Models

More-sophisticated mathematical models include the effects of changing fluid and rock properties, pressure histories, well-producing characteristics, and reservoir spatial variations into the analysis process. The outcome of these calculations can be presented as 1-, 2-, or 3-dimensional spatial analysis of the reservoir operating under different well-configuration and depletion conditions. These studies are more time-consuming and costly, and they call for considerably more information than is required for a study of the decline-curve characteristics.

Any reservoir study is driven by three basic criteria: time and effort that can be allotted to the study, quantity and quality of available data, and usage of the results. A reconnaissance study using government records of offset operators' production history is conducted in a much shorter time span and with much less quantitative information than expended for an in-depth evaluation of the waterflood potential of a complete field in which you have control.

The types and quality of information are functions of a number of variables. For instance, geographical location and country, whether the field is wholly owned or jointly operated, and the net value of the produced product affect the quality and quantity of information. The need for good-quality information must be balanced with the economic worth of the property and the time frame allowed for conducting the study. There is usually little information available on marginal wells, while there may be a plethora of data on good-quality fields. Each situation is different, and deciding the proper balance between time, available field information, and the goals of the study is the first step when developing a plan of investigation.

The science of forecasting future production and reservoir evaluation can be divided into four areas that roughly correspond to the allotted time and effort to be expended as well as the quantity and quality of information.

1.2 Volumetric Calculations

Static log and core analysis measurements form the basis for calculating original oil- or gas-in-place. Reserves are determined with empirically determined recovery factors or by a "rule of thumb" developed from knowledge of a particular area. These static properties do not permit dynamic performance forecasting.

The strengths of the volumetric calculations are a low-cost, easily understood evaluation technique for determining in-place hydrocarbon values, and isopach maps that can be combined with structural maps to provide a comprehensive picture for estimating reservoir or field extent.

The weaknesses of the volumetric calculations are as follows: The results are a function of well spacing and the quality of porosity and saturation values; the maps are unable to forecast future productivity and the degree of drainage heterogeneity; and it is difficult to predict recovery from either a layered or naturally fractured reservoir, or in reservoirs with commingled production.

1.3 Decline Curves

The equation of a line is fitted to a historical production decline curve. Future performance is calculated by manipulating the equation to solve for rate, time, or cumulative production. Reserves are calculated from the performance prediction.

The strengths of the analysis of production decline curves are that production data are widely available, and that the method is low-cost and time-efficient as well as being easily programmed for operation on personal computers.

The weaknesses of the analysis of production decline curves are as follows: A match of the historical data with the equation of a line represents a mathematical relationship (for most cases, reservoir character cannot be quantitatively inferred from the shape of the curve); changes in operating conditions usually alter the shape of the decline curve; and interpretation of future performance is difficult in low-permeability, multilayered, or fractured reservoirs because of the highly variable and uncertain effects of crossflow. Changes in these operating conditions and any potential changes must be taken into account when developing the equation replicating a production decline curve and, more particularly, when predicting performance. A decline curve does not necessarily satisfy a material balance for this type of reservoir.

1.4 The Material Balance

Pressure-dependent rock and fluid properties are included in a reservoir material-balance-type equation. The material-balance, tank-type model is based on the conservation of mass, which does not account for variable flow conditions.

The strengths of material-balance-type calculations are as follows: Pressure-dependent reservoir rock and fluid properties, as well as the production history are included in a reservoir model; it is a low-cost and time-efficient analysis method that is easily programmed for personal computers; and the method can be easily applied to a moderate-to-high permeability field to determine the depletion efficiency.

The major weakness of the material balance method is the need to apply a recovery factor to calculate reserves. Vertical and areal variations in the reservoir character must be included as part of the reserves calculations. Recovery factors should be applied only to relatively homogeneous, modest-sized reservoirs in which the producing zone exhibits $k > 100$ md for oil reservoirs and $k > 1$ md for gas reservoirs.

1.5 Reservoir Simulation

The reservoir is divided into a grid system. The material balance, diffusivity flow equation, and equation of state are combined into an iterative process to calculate the influence of the depletion history for each cell in the system.

The strengths of reservoir simulation type calculations are as follows: They can be applied to a 2D or 3D system and with widely changing fluid composition; they permit all possible variables to be included in the model; and it is easy to study the effects of reservoir heterogeneity and variation on future performance.

The weaknesses of reservoir simulation models are as follows: A person skilled in the mechanics of running the model to be involved in the study is generally required; the models are complicated and require considerable time, effort, and expense to run; and these models require a comprehensive array of field data. The field model is often simplified by forcing reservoir heterogeneities and geology to fit the computer model. Therefore, the results are no better than the quality of the input data. There is an old adage, "what you input is what you get—garbage in, garbage out."

1.6 Historical Perspective

Two seminal investigators provided the basis for analyzing production histories with decline curves. Arps (1945, 1956) coalesced all previous work into an inclusive and unified set of empirically derived equations.

Decline curves were categorized as exponential, hyperbolic, and harmonic in nature. Expressions relating rate, time, and cumulative production interactions in terms of a general equation of a line were defined. Fetkovich et al. (1987) divided decline curves into transient- and boundary-dominated flow categories and provided a set of type curves to facilitate the interpretation process. Work conducted principally by Fetkovich (Fetkovich et al. 1987; Fetkovich 1980) and Camacho-Velazquez and Raghavan (1989) showed that the mode of depletion could often be inferred from the shape of the production decline curve.

It has long been recognized that declining reservoir pressure causes oil or gas wells to suffer a loss in production rate. This decline rate can be expressed in terms of the chord of a straight line drawn between any two production values, or the total production history can be divided into a series of chord approximations of equal time intervals. **Fig. 1.1** illustrates the effect of dividing a rate-time curve into a series of straight lines of decreasing slope. An alternate method uses a differential equation to express the equation of the line in terms of an instantaneous decline rate. The equation of the line begins at some initial producing rate q_i and decline rate D_i, which may not necessarily be the same as the historical values.

Arnold and Anderson (1908), in a study of a number of California oil fields in 1908, were apparently the first to realize that the loss of production could be expressed as a constant fraction of the production rate. This production rate loss, measured during a specified time span, was defined as the decline rate.

The following development relates an initial rate, q_i, to a later rate, q_2, to derive relevant decline-curve equations. In actuality, the initial producing rate can be selected at any point on the curve. This point is often denoted as q_1. Any initial rate can be chosen as long as the proper time interval between the first and last rates is included in the calculation procedure.

The first reference to plotting production data on graph paper, by Day (1909), also recognized the concept of a well-drainage area. This study of New York and Pennsylvania oil fields found that increasing the number of producing wells did not necessarily increase the field-producing rate. Vance (1961) showed that production data could be plotted as a percentage of the previous year's production. Eq. 1.1 expresses this incremental rate loss concept in mathematical terms when a first rate is defined as q_1 and a subsequent rate as q_2. The 1/time units reflect any two producing rate values spanning a particular time period. By convention, the rate differences span a 1-year time period. The fraction is usually multiplied by 100 and given a negative sign (−) to express the decline rate in terms of a positive %/yr.

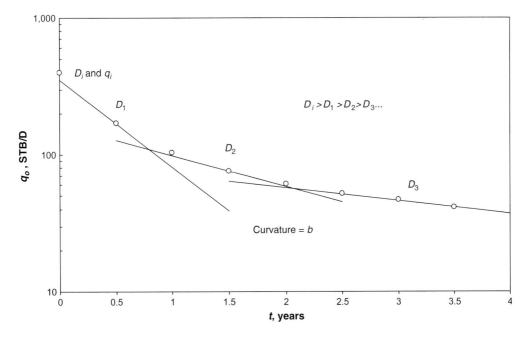

Fig. 1.1—Dividing a curved rate-time plot into a series of chords of decreasing slope. The fitted curve begins at some initial producing and decline rate, which may or may not coincide with the field data. The degree of curvature of the production history is a function of the exponent b term. A continuous straight line reflects a b = 0 value.

$$D = \frac{\frac{q_1 - q_2}{\Delta t}}{q_1} = \frac{\frac{\Delta q}{\Delta t}}{q_1}, \frac{1}{\text{time}}. \quad \dots\dots\dots\dots\dots\dots\dots\dots\dots\dots\dots\dots\dots\dots\dots \quad (1.1)$$

Lewis and Beal (1918) recognized that decline curves often fit a hyperbolic equation. Cutler (1924) determined that a constant or exponential decline rate did not apply to all field cases. A hyperbolic curve appeared to fit the production data accumulated from 149 fields covering 14 states better than fits that could be achieved by an exponential curve.

Johnson and Bollens (1927) introduced the concept of loss ratio. Eq. 1.2 shows the loss ratio expressed in incremental and differential forms. The term is defined as the fractional change in the production rate when the production loss measured during a time period is located in the denominator. The interval between the two producing rates defines the time frame during which the loss ratio occurred.

$$R = \frac{q_2}{\frac{q_1 - q_2}{\Delta t}} = \frac{q_2}{\frac{\Delta q}{\Delta t}} = \frac{q_2}{\frac{dq}{dt}}, \text{ time}. \quad \dots\dots\dots\dots\dots\dots\dots\dots\dots\dots\dots\dots\dots\dots \quad (1.2)$$

Note: There is an inverse relationship between Eqs. 1.1 and 1.2, and the reference rate was changed from the initial rate, q_i, in Eq. 1.1 to the last rate in Eq. 1.2, q_2. The Johnson and Bollens (1927) paper showed that a constant loss ratio implied a constant percentage decline, while a constant difference in the loss ratios implied either a fit of a hyperbolic curve or some form of a power equation. Calculate performance with a rearranged form of Eq. 1.2 after calculating the loss ratio for each time step.

Marsh (1928) introduced the concept that a rate-cumulative production plot is a straight line. This relationship is equivalent to an exponential decline curve as long as the operating conditions do not change. Pirson (1935) applied the loss ratio approach to form fundamental equations describing exponential and hyperbolic declines.

1.7 The Arps Empirical Equations

Arps applied a mathematical treatment to coalesce these earlier concepts to unify the theory on the rate-time-cumulative production characteristics of production decline curves (Arps 1945, 1956).

Express the rate of change of the flow rate in terms of the decline rate, D. Eq. 1.3a presents the general form of the equation. Inclusion of the negative sign converts the negative decline rate value to a positive expression.

$$D = -\frac{1}{q}\frac{dq}{dt}. \quad \dots\dots\dots\dots\dots\dots\dots\dots\dots\dots\dots\dots\dots\dots\dots\dots\dots\dots \quad (1.3a)$$

Express the previous equation in differential form:

$$D = -\frac{d(\ln q)}{dt}. \quad \dots\dots\dots\dots\dots\dots\dots\dots\dots\dots\dots\dots\dots\dots\dots\dots\dots \quad (1.3b)$$

Define the b-exponent term as the time-rate-change of the reciprocal of the decline rate:

$$b = \frac{d(1/D)}{dt} = \text{constant}. \quad \dots\dots\dots\dots\dots\dots\dots\dots\dots\dots\dots\dots\dots\dots \quad (1.4a)$$

Eq. 1.4b shows the first derivative of Eq. 1.3a:

$$b = -\frac{d}{dt}\left(\frac{q}{dq/dt}\right) = \text{constant}. \quad \dots\dots\dots\dots\dots\dots\dots\dots\dots\dots\dots \quad (1.4b)$$

The b-exponent term should remain constant as the producing rate declines from an initial value to some later value. However, in many instances, changes in operating conditions cause these values to change during the life of the property. This variation of character often requires the well history to be divided into a series of producing segments, with each segment representing a time of common character or exponent value.

Equations representing exponential, hyperbolic, and harmonic production declines are developed from the basic definitions expressed as Eqs. 1.3 and 1.4. Integrating Eq. 1.4a over the range 0 to t and defining the initial decline rate at $t = 0$ as D_i produces the following relationship:

$$D = \frac{D_i}{1 + bD_i t} . \quad\dots\dots\dots\dots\dots\dots\dots\dots\dots\dots\dots\dots\dots\dots\dots \quad (1.5)$$

Substituting Eq. 1.5 into Eq. 1.3b results in the following:

$$-\frac{d(\ln q)}{dt} = \frac{D_i}{1 + bD_i t} . \quad\dots\dots\dots\dots\dots\dots\dots\dots\dots\dots\dots\dots \quad (1.6)$$

Two cases for the exponent term should be considered. These cases are when $b = 0$, and when $b \neq 0$. The following discussion develops the rate and rate-time equations appropriate to either of these two conditions.

1.7.1 The $b = 0$ Case. Eq. 1.5 reduces to the equality $D = D_i$ when $b = 0$. Decline rate is not a function of time, because the value remains constant throughout the time interval. Convention replaces the theoretically correct D_i term with D because of the $D = D_i$ identity. Eq. 1.6 reduces to the following form for the constant decline rate case:

$$D = -\frac{d(\ln q)}{dt} . \quad\dots\dots\dots\dots\dots\dots\dots\dots\dots\dots\dots\dots\dots\dots \quad (1.7)$$

Integrating Eq. 1.7 over the range 0 to t develops a producing rate expression:

$$q_2 = q_i \exp(-Dt). \quad\dots\dots\dots\dots\dots\dots\dots\dots\dots\dots\dots\dots\dots \quad (1.8)$$

1.7.2 The $b \neq 0$ Case. Integrating Eq. 1.6 over the 0 to t range and including the definition for the initial producing rate results in a rate equation defining the equation of the line for all cases when $b \neq 0$:

$$q(t) = q_2 = \frac{q_i}{\left(1 + bD_i t\right)^{1/b}} . \quad\dots\dots\dots\dots\dots\dots\dots\dots\dots\dots\dots \quad (1.9)$$

Combining Eqs. 1.3a, 1.6, and 1.9 results in the producing rate-decline rate relationship shown in Eq. 1.10. The equation is also valid for the constant decline case when $b = 0$, because $D = D_i$ for this instance.

$$D = -\frac{1}{q}\frac{dq}{dt} = D_i \left(\frac{q}{q_i}\right)^b . \quad\dots\dots\dots\dots\dots\dots\dots\dots\dots\dots \quad (1.10)$$

The following discussion applies the previously developed general equations to the definitions for exponential, hyperbolic, and the special case of harmonic production decline curves. Arps (1945) defined $b = 0$ for the exponential case, $0 < b < 1$ for the hyperbolic case, and $b = 1$ for the harmonic case. These equations are presented in terms of rate, time, and cumulative recovery expressions.

1.8 Exponential Equations

Expressing Eq. 1.8 in logarithmic terms and arranging in the form of the equation of a straight line results in Eq. 1.11. The plotting variables for the straight line are: "y" axis: $\ln q_2$ and the "x" axis: t. The outcome variables are: "y" intercept: $\ln q_i$ while the slope of the line is $-D$.

$$\ln q_2 = -Dt + \ln q_i . \quad\dots\dots\dots\dots\dots\dots\dots\dots\dots\dots\dots\dots\dots \quad (1.11)$$

Eq. 1.8 can be rearranged to solve for the continuous decline rate. The constant decline rate for the exponential case permits the initial rate to be selected anywhere on the curve. This rate is often denoted as q_1.

$$D = \frac{\ln\left(\dfrac{q_1}{q_2}\right)}{t}. \quad\ldots\ldots\ldots\ldots\ldots\ldots\ldots\ldots\ldots\ldots\ldots\ldots\ldots\ldots\ldots\ldots\ldots\ldots\ldots\quad (1.12)$$

Rearrange Eq. 1.12 to provide a time relationship spanning the period between the two rates as follows:

$$t = \frac{\ln\left(\dfrac{q_1}{q_2}\right)}{D}. \quad\ldots\ldots\ldots\ldots\ldots\ldots\ldots\ldots\ldots\ldots\ldots\ldots\ldots\ldots\ldots\ldots\ldots\ldots\ldots\quad (1.13)$$

The generalized equation for estimating cumulative production is as follows:

$$Q_p = \int_0^t q\,dt. \quad\ldots\ldots\ldots\ldots\ldots\ldots\ldots\ldots\ldots\ldots\ldots\ldots\ldots\ldots\ldots\ldots\ldots\ldots\ldots\ldots\quad (1.14)$$

Substituting Eq. 1.8 into Eq. 1.14 results in an expression for the exponential case. Integrating this equation over the $t > 0$ range results in an expression for calculating cumulative production:

$$Q_p = \frac{q_i}{D}\left[1 - \exp(-Dt)\right]. \quad\ldots\ldots\ldots\ldots\ldots\ldots\ldots\ldots\ldots\ldots\ldots\ldots\ldots\ldots\quad (1.15)$$

Include the rate Eq. 1.8 into a rearranged form of Eq. 1.15 to convert the cumulative production equation to a simplified form.

$$Q_p = \frac{q_i - q_2}{D}. \quad\ldots\ldots\ldots\ldots\ldots\ldots\ldots\ldots\ldots\ldots\ldots\ldots\ldots\ldots\ldots\ldots\ldots\ldots\ldots\quad (1.16)$$

Rearrange Eq. 1.16 to a form replicating the equation of a straight line. The plotting variables for the straight line are the "y" axis, $q2$, and the "x" axis, Q_p. The outcome variables are "y" intercept, q_i, and the slope of the line $-D$.

$$q_2 = -DQ_p + q_i. \quad\ldots\ldots\ldots\ldots\ldots\ldots\ldots\ldots\ldots\ldots\ldots\ldots\ldots\ldots\ldots\ldots\quad (1.17)$$

Assume the production rate declines from $q_i \to 0$ to calculate the theoretical maximum cumulative production for an exponential decline curve. Eq. 1.16 reduces to the following form:

$$Q_{p_{max}} = \frac{q_i}{D}. \quad\ldots\ldots\ldots\ldots\ldots\ldots\ldots\ldots\ldots\ldots\ldots\ldots\ldots\ldots\ldots\ldots\ldots\ldots\quad (1.18)$$

1.9 Hyperbolic Equations

The hyperbolic case was defined by Arps to encompass the $0 < b < 1$ range. Rearranging Eq. 1.9 provides a means to calculate the time interval spanning an initial and final rate for the hyperbolic case.

$$t = \frac{\left(\dfrac{q_i}{q_2}\right)^b - 1}{bD_i}. \quad\ldots\ldots\ldots\ldots\ldots\ldots\ldots\ldots\ldots\ldots\ldots\ldots\ldots\ldots\ldots\ldots\quad (1.19)$$

A rearranged form of Eq. 1.10 results in a producing rate-decline rate relationship for the hyperbolic case as follows:

$$\frac{D_i}{D_2} = \left(\frac{q_i}{q_2}\right)^b. \quad\ldots\ldots\ldots\ldots\ldots\ldots\ldots\ldots\ldots\ldots\ldots\ldots\ldots\ldots\ldots\ldots\ldots\ldots\quad (1.20)$$

Eq. 1.20 reverts to the harmonic case when $b = 1$ and to the exponential case when $b = 0$. Substituting the rate Eq. 1.9 into Eq. 1.14 and integrating over $0 \leq t$ time interval spanning the time from initial to final conditions results in a cumulative production expression.

$$Q_p = \frac{q_i}{D_i(1-b)}\left[1 - \frac{1}{(1+bD_it)^{(1-b)/b}}\right]. \dots\dots\dots\dots\dots\dots (1.21)$$

Substitution of the rate Eq. 1.9 back into the previous equation results in Eq. 1.22.

$$Q_p = \frac{q_i}{D_i(1-b)}\left[1 - \left(\frac{q_2}{q_i}\right)^{1-b}\right]. \dots\dots\dots\dots\dots\dots (1.22)$$

Assume $q_2 = 0$ to express Eq. 1.22 in terms of a theoretical maximum cumulative production value.

$$Q_{p\,max} = \frac{q_i}{D_i(1-b)}. \dots\dots\dots\dots\dots\dots (1.23)$$

Note: There is a complexity of the equations for predicting performance for the hyperbolic case. An exponent term, initial decline, and producing rate must be determined for each particular case.

1.10 Harmonic Equations

The harmonic case is a restricted version of a hyperbolic case, because the exponent term was defined by Arps (1945) as $b = 1$. The generalized decline-rate-producing rate relationship shown as Eq. 1.20 reverts to the following form for the harmonic case because the exponent term equals 1:

$$\frac{D_i}{D_2} = \frac{q_i}{q_2}. \dots\dots\dots\dots\dots\dots (1.24)$$

The producing rate Eq. 1.9 changes to the following form for the harmonic case:

$$q_2 = \frac{q_i}{1 + D_it}. \dots\dots\dots\dots\dots\dots (1.25)$$

Rearrange Eq. 1.25 to solve for the time difference between an initial and a subsequent rate.

$$t = \frac{q_i - q_2}{D_iq_2}. \dots\dots\dots\dots\dots\dots (1.26)$$

Substitute Eq. 1.25 into the integral expression Eq. 1.14 and integrate over the $0 \leq t$ range spanning the production decline from some earlier value to a later value to develop an expression for cumulative recovery.

$$Q_p = \frac{q_i}{D_i}\ln(1 + D_it). \dots\dots\dots\dots\dots\dots (1.27)$$

Simplify the previous equation by combining with Eq. 1.25.

$$Q_p = \frac{q_i}{D_i}\ln\left(\frac{q_i}{q_2}\right). \dots\dots\dots\dots\dots\dots (1.28)$$

Rewrite Eq. 1.28 in the following form:

$$\ln q_2 = \ln q_i - \frac{Q_p D_i}{q_i}. \dots\dots\dots\dots\dots\dots (1.29)$$

TABLE 1.1—SUMMARY OF ARPS AND DIMENSIONLESS EQUATIONS				
	Decline Rate	Producing Rate, q	Elapsed Time, t	Cumulative Production, Q_p
Exponential $b = 0$	$\dfrac{\ln\left(\dfrac{q_i}{q_2}\right)}{t}$	$q_i \exp(-Dt)$	$\dfrac{\ln\left(\dfrac{q_i}{q_2}\right)}{D}$	$\dfrac{q_i - q_2}{D}$
Hyperbolic $0 < b < 1$	$\dfrac{D_i}{D_2} = \left(\dfrac{q_i}{q_2}\right)^b$	$\dfrac{q_i}{(1+bD_it)^{\frac{1}{b}}}$	$\dfrac{\left(\dfrac{q_i}{q_2}\right)^b - 1}{bD_i}$	$\dfrac{q_i}{D_i(1-b)}\left[1-\left(\dfrac{q_2}{q_i}\right)^{1-b}\right]$
Harmonic $b = 1$	$\dfrac{D_i}{D_2} = \dfrac{q_i}{q_2}$	$\dfrac{q_i}{1+D_it}$	$\dfrac{q_i - q_2}{D_iq_2}$	$\dfrac{q_i}{D_i}\ln\left(\dfrac{q_i}{q_2}\right)$
Dimensionless		$q_{Dd} = \dfrac{q_2}{q_i}$	$t_{Dd} = D_it$	$Q_{pDd} = \dfrac{Q_p}{q_i/D_i}$

Notice:
- The q_i and decline rate D terms define the properties of the exponential curve.
- The q_i and initial decline rate D_i identify the initial points of the harmonic curve.
- The b, q_i, and D_i must be determined to find the shape and initial point of the hyperbolic curve.

The equation of a straight line can be fitted to Eq. 1.29. The plotting variables for the straight line are y axis, $\ln q$, and x axis, Q_p. The outcome variables are y intercept, $\ln q_i$, and slope of the line, $-\dfrac{D_i}{q_i}$.

Table 1.1 summarizes the decline rate, producing rate, time, and cumulative production equations for the exponential, hyperbolic, and harmonic decline curves as dimensionless relationships applied later in this development.

1.11 Bounds of the Arps Equations

Theoretically, the b-exponent term included in the generalized rate-time Eq. 1.9 could vary in a positive or negative manner as long as $b \neq 0$. This equation reverts to the exponential form, Eq. 1.8, when $b = 0$. A negative b-exponent value implies an increasing rate, which is sometimes observed in the study of early coal gas production data when gradual unloading of pore water increases the relative permeability to gas. However, this phenomenon is not germane to a generalized discussion of oil and gas production decline curves. The following development shows that the Arps equations are truly appropriate only within the $0 \leq b <$ range. Note: The harmonic curve does not fit this definition.

The hyperbolic cumulative production equation, Eq. 1.21, reverts to the following form, because the $(1-b)$ value is always > 0 for this case:

$$Q_p = \frac{q_i}{D_i(1-b)}\left[1 - \frac{1}{\left(1+bD_it\right)^{(1-b)/b}}\right]. \quad \dotfill \quad (1.30)$$

This equation suggests that production extends to infinite time; hence, cumulative production is also infinite. Completely unbounded reservoirs are a physical impossibility, although one would hope to find it in the best of all worlds. The previous statement shows why the b-exponent term cannot be greater than 1, because completely unbounded conditions are never encountered. A similar physical contradiction is achieved when the idea of infinite time is applied to the harmonic cumulative recovery equation shown as Eq. 1.27.

These studies show that the decline exponent must vary over the range $0 \leq b < 1$ to apply the Arps curves in a practical sense. The harmonic case should be used only with reservations, because forward extrapolation results in an infinite cumulative recovery estimate.

1.12 Dimensionless Groups

The following dimensionless time, rate, and cumulative recovery groups are defined and summarized in Table 1.1. These dimensionless groups are applied for the type-curve approaches discussed in later chapters.

Define the dimensionless rate as some later rate divided by an earlier producing rate.

$$q_{Dd} = \frac{q_2}{q_i}. \dots\dots\dots\dots\dots\dots\dots\dots\dots\dots\dots\dots\dots\dots\dots\dots\dots\dots\dots\dots\dots\dots\dots \tag{1.31}$$

Define dimensionless time as the continuous decline rate, the dimensions of which are 1/time, multiplied by a time interval when both time intervals are the same units.

$$t_{Dd} = D_i t. \dots\dots\dots\dots\dots\dots\dots\dots\dots\dots\dots\dots\dots\dots\dots\dots\dots\dots\dots\dots\dots\dots\dots\dots\dots \tag{1.32}$$

Multiply cumulative production by the ratio of initial decline rate and production rate to define a dimensionless cumulative production. Remember: The volume and time units must be consistent.

$$Q_{pDd} = \frac{D_i Q_p}{q_i}. \dots\dots\dots\dots\dots\dots\dots\dots\dots\dots\dots\dots\dots\dots\dots\dots\dots\dots\dots\dots\dots \tag{1.33}$$

1.13 Curve Characteristics

Arps exponential, hyperbolic, and harmonic curves are plotted in rectangular and semilogarithmic coordinate systems to illustrate three instances of straightline relationships.

Fig. 1.2 compares the general shapes of the rate-time plots of the Arps exponential, harmonic, and hyperbolic curves. The $b = 0.5$ line illustrates the hyperbolic curve, even though it may lie anywhere between the exponential and harmonic boundary curves for different b values. All the rate-time curves trend in a concave, upward manner. Extrapolation of curved lines into the future is laborious and uncertain.

Eq. 1.16 indicates that the exponential curve shown in the rate-cumulative recovery plot of **Fig. 1.3** is a straight line, while the hyperbolic and harmonic lines are curved when plotted in the same coordinate system.

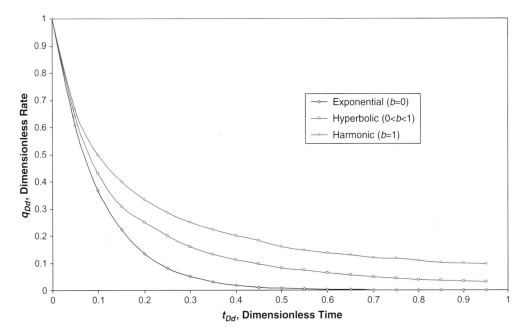

Fig. 1.2—Exponential and harmonic decline curves bound the range of the hyperbolic decline curve. Note: All lines are curves on the rectangular rate-time plot.

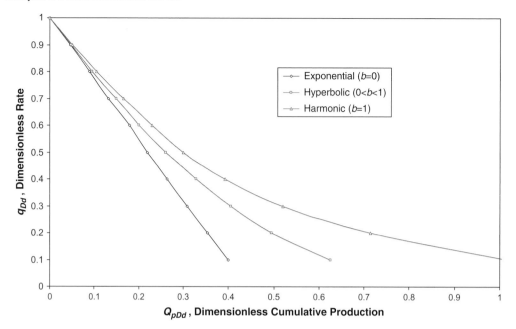

Fig. 1.3—The exponential curve forms a straight line when plotted on a rate-cumulative production plot. The hyperbolic and harmonic declines remain curved.

The straightline character of the exponential rate-cumulative recovery plot readily lends itself to predicting performance with a high degree of accuracy.

Fig. 1.4 shows that the exponential semilog rate-time curve is a straight line, while the hyperbolic and harmonic decline lines are curved. Eqs. 1.8, 1.12, and 1.17 reflect the straightline relationship for the exponential case. Logarithms tend to compress larger valued data. Compressing the data induces a damping effect that results in an apparent smoothing of the production curve at later times.

Fig. 1.5 compares the three Arps curves presented on a semilog rate-cumulative production plot. In this case, Eq. 1.29, developed for the harmonic curve, results in a straight line, while the exponential and hyperbolic declines are concave downward.

The straightline properties of the exponential decline for rate-cumulative production and semilog rate-time plots, and of the harmonic decline for a semilog rate-cumulative production plot, provide a ready method for extrapolating into the future for these particular instances. Unfortunately, one is not so lucky for the hyperbolic curve. Logarithmic scale rate-time and rate-cumulative recovery plots result in all curves trending in a concave, downward manner for this case. Plotting techniques, such as that of Fetkovich (1980), commonly use a form of a log-log plot.

Arps (1945) represented production decline curves in terms of exponential, hyperbolic, and harmonic equations. In all cases, it was tacitly assumed that one of these definitions could be fitted to an extended production history for extension into the future.

The three straightline representations for the rate-time and rate-cumulative production plots for the exponential and harmonic cases afford a reasonable vehicle for extrapolating future performance. However, there are no straightline relationships for the hyperbolic case. Discussions in Chapter 4 and Chapter 5 develop the Arps approach to determine equations for these three types of curves, while application of the type-curve approach is discussed in Chapter 3.

1.14 Economic Limit (EL)

Production from an oil or gas property is usually extended to the point where the net income derived from sales of the production stream is equal to the maintenance expense. There is no useful purpose for continuing production beyond this point; therefore, the well is shut in or abandoned at this point.

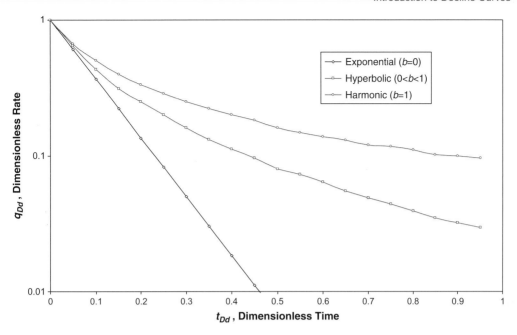

Fig. 1.4—The straightline properties of the exponential curve when plotted on a logarithmic rate-coordinate time scale. The hyperbolic and harmonic declines remain curved.

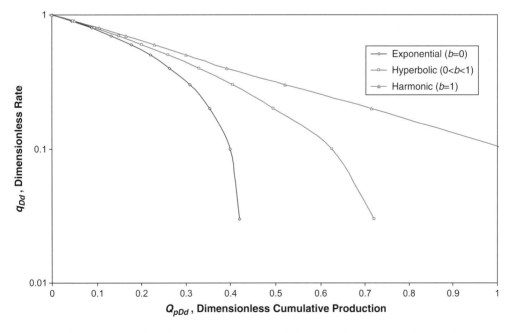

Fig. 1.5—The straightline properties of the harmonic curve plotted on a logarithmic rate-coordinate cumulative production scale. The exponential and hyperbolic declines remain curved for the same coordinate system.

Expenses to produce a well are classified as overhead, direct well-operating costs, and additional expenditure costs. Overhead expenses cover the general and administrative costs (G&A). The decision to either abandon a well or keep it producing should not necessarily include the proportionate cost of the allocated overhead. These costs probably continue even if the well is abandoned, because total G&A costs are reapportioned out to other wells in the operation if a particular well is shut in.

Direct well-operating expenses cover the cost of supervision by the field personnel, monthly pumping and chemical treatment costs, and any other ordinary maintenance expenses. Periodic but significant expenditures, such as pulling rods, fixing casing leaks, fracturing, or any type of well work, should not be included in an estimate of the operating expense. A separate economic analysis must be conducted to evaluate the utility of spending additional money on the proposed well work.

Net income is the income remaining after operating costs, royalties, and direct production taxes are deducted from the gross income. Income tax may or may not be a part of the net income statement. Both oil and gas sales should be included in the case of an oil well, while gas and condensate sales should be included in the case of a gas well.

Expense costs are charged to the property. These costs are usually expressed on a per-month basis or in some other unit of time. Allocating costs as expenses per unit of production, such as USD/stock-tank barrel (STB) or USD/million standard cubic feet (MMscf), causes the expenses to be compared to the production rate. Well costs are not necessarily a function of the production rate but are a function of maintenance and operational costs attributed to each well.

1.15 Reserves-to-Production Ratio

The reserves-to-production ratio, R/P, provides a handy but qualitative screening tool for rapidly evaluating wells or small reservoirs when there is little available information. The method works best in moderate-to-high-productivity sands and small-to-moderate-sized reservoirs. Eq. 1.34 defines the basic equation when the production rate is assumed to be the average rate.

$$\frac{R}{P} = \frac{Q_p}{q}, \text{time.} \quad \dots\dots\dots\dots\dots\dots\dots\dots\dots\dots\dots\dots\dots\dots\dots\dots\dots (1.34)$$

Rearrange the cumulative recovery equation for the exponential decline curve, Eq. 1.16, to the following form:

$$\frac{Q_p}{q_1 - q_2} = \frac{1}{D}, \text{time.} \quad \dots\dots\dots\dots\dots\dots\dots\dots\dots\dots\dots\dots\dots\dots\dots (1.35)$$

Combining the two previous equations and assuming the $q_1 - q_2$ term is equivalent to an average producing rate results in a relationship defining the R/P ratio as the reciprocal of the exponential decline rate.

$$\frac{R}{P} = \frac{1}{D} \quad \dots\dots\dots\dots\dots\dots\dots\dots\dots\dots\dots\dots\dots\dots\dots\dots\dots\dots\dots\dots (1.36)$$

Two examples of this inverse relationship between reserves and the exponential decline rate are: (i) if $R/P = 10$ years, then $D = 10\%/yr$; and (ii) if $D = 20\%/yr$, then $R/P = 5$ years. Application of Eq. 1.36 assumes the R/P ratio remains constant during the predictive period.

1.15.1 Problem. What are the reserves of a Gulf of Mexico well when a 30%/yr exponential decline rate is expected? The initial rate for the first year of production is 73,000 STB/yr, while the EL is 3,700 STB/yr. Develop a production schedule for the case when the well R/P value is assumed to remain constant.

Solution. The first step calculates total reserves and the reserves expected to be produced down to the EL. Applying a rearranged form of Eq. 1.35:

$$N_{p\,max} = \frac{q_1 - q_2}{D} = \frac{(73 - 0)\,\text{thousand STB/yr}}{0.3/yr} = 243.3 \text{ thousand STB}$$

$$N_p \text{ to EL} = \frac{q_1 - q_2}{D} = \frac{(73 - 3.7)\,\text{thousand STB/yr}}{0.3/yr} = 231 \text{ thousand STB}$$

Calculate a Rate Schedule. Calculate yearly production with Eq. 1.36. The complete production schedule listed in **Table 1.2** indicates an 8.4-year well life. The example calculation for the Year 2 estimate is as follows:

Year	q (thousand STB/yr)	N_p (thousand STB)
1	73.0	73.0
2	47.4	120.4
3	33.2	153.6
4	23.2	176.8
5	16.3	193.1
6	11.4	204.5
7	8.0	212.5
8	5.6	218.1
9	3.9	222.0

TABLE 1.2—R/P EXAMPLE PROBLEM

$$\text{Rate} = D(\text{Reserves}) = (0.3/\text{yr})(231 - 73) = 0.3(158) = 47.4 \text{ thousand STB/yr}.$$

In actuality, the R/P ratio often changes during the life of a property. The historical variation of the R/P value is often used to analyze the yearly reserves summaries of producing properties, particularly in the case in which only limited reservoir information is available. The following rules of thumb may be established: First, an increasing R/P may indicate that reserves are overstated; second, a decreasing R/P may indicate that reserves are understated, because the decline rate is becoming flatter. A closer study of the property should be conducted in either case.

The preceding discussion shows that the R/P concept can be related to an exponential decline curve. Properties producing from similar geographical and geological horizons should display similar R/P ratios. If one property displays a value different from its neighbors, then it should be studied to determine the cause for this variation. The R/P concept is a useful tool for evaluating well-workover jobs. Generally, R/P ratios of 9 or greater should merit further review, because they indicate a rather long-lived well. The property could be underdeveloped, or the reserves could be overstated. Conversely, low R/P ratios on the order of 1 to 4 probably indicate that the property is near the end of its productive life.

1.16 The Diffusivity Equation

Most early investigators assumed that the equation of a line could be found to represent a production decline curve; however, this curve did not reflect any particular type of reservoir performance.

In actuality, an exponential decline curve reflects production response from a reservoir of limited extent and producing from an essentially constant compressibility system. Therefore, the total volume of hydrocarbons located within the drainage area influences the performance history. This observation was initially observed by Arps (1956) and Brons (1963), and theoretically verified by Fetkovich (1980), who showed that the solution to the diffusivity equation for constant pressure, boundary-dominated depletion conditions is the same form as the Arps equation for an exponential decline curve (Campbell 1959).

The diffusivity equation describes fluid flow through a porous medium. Solutions to the partial differential equation are defined by the boundary values forming the basis for the derivation. Physical boundary conditions are imposed at the inner and outer boundary of the system. The outer boundary (defined as the reservoir limit) can be classified as finite and closed, finite with a partially sealing boundary, or infinite. Either constant bottomhole flowing pressure or constant rate conditions are set at the inner boundary, which is assumed to be at the perforations. Dimensionless relationships form a bridge between these mathematical solutions and field studies.

van Everdingen and Hurst (1949) presented a series of dimensionless tables and figures reflecting the changes occurring in infinite and bounded reservoirs operating under both constant bottomhole pressures and constant rates. Equations are presented to relate the dimensionless solutions to dimensioned field conditions.

Eqs. 1.37 and 1.38 are the dimensionless-field value relationships established for the van Everdingen and Hurst (1949) solutions. The dimensionless wellbore pressure (p_{wD}) of the constant terminal flow-rate solution is given in Eq. 1.37 in terms of conventional oilfield units for slightly compressible liquid flow in the reservoir. The corresponding dimensionless wellbore flow rate (q_{wD}) that corresponds to the terminal pressure solution is defined in terms of conventional oilfield units for liquid flow cases in Eq. 1.38.

Constant-rate solution: $p_{wD} = \dfrac{kh\left(p_i - p_{wf}\right)}{141.2q\mu B}$. .... (1.37)

Constant-pressure solution: $q_{wD} = \dfrac{141.2q\mu B}{kh\left(p_i - p_{wf}\right)}$. .... (1.38)

The rate term units are STB/D. The van Everdingen and Hurst (1949) solutions are presented as dimensionless correlation terms representing the relative reservoir size and time elapsed from the start of the disturbance. Eq. 1.39 expresses the dimensionless-time real-time relationship when time units are days.

$$t_D = \frac{0.00633kt}{\phi\mu c_t r_w^{\ 2}}.$$ .... (1.39)

Eq. 1.40 relates the radius of the outermost reservoir boundary r_e to the innermost boundary, which for this case is the wellbore radius r_w. This dimensionless expression furnishes an estimate of the relative drainage volume.

$$r_{eD} = \frac{r_e}{r_w}.$$ .... (1.40)

Fig. 1.6 illustrates the van Everdingen and Hurst (1949) dimensionless well flow rate-time, constant-pressure solutions for infinite acting and $r_{eD} = 2$, 4, and 8 reservoir sizes. **Fig. 1.7** illustrates the corresponding van Everdingen and Hurst dimensionless cumulative production-time solutions for the infinite-acting and bounded reservoir cases presented in Fig. 1.6.

The definition of the dimensionless cumulative production, Q_{pD}, which corresponds to the van Everdingen and Hurst (1949) liquid flow solution for a constant pressure drawdown, is given in Eq. 1.41. The oil cumulative production in this expression is given in units of STB.

$$Q_{pD} = \frac{0.8936N_p B}{\phi c_t h r_w^{\ 2}\left(p_i - p_{wf}\right)}.$$ .... (1.41)

Figs. 1.6 and 1.7 can be divided into the following three parts:

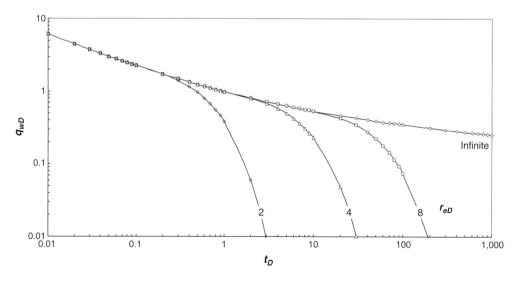

Fig. 1.6—Illustrating the logarithmic flow rate-time plot of four of the van Everdingen and Hurst constant-pressure solutions. The dimensionless well flow rate mirrors the infinite-acting reservoir curve until the outer boundary begins to affect the well performance. The figure shows how flow conditions can be divided into infinite-acting, transition, and boundary-dominated cases. Adapted from van Everdingen and Hurst (1949).

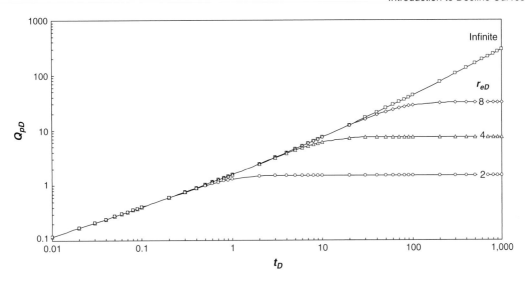

Fig. 1.7—Illustrating the logarithmic cumulative production-time plot of four of the van Everdingen and Hurst constant-pressure solutions. The dimensionless cumulative production mirrors the infinite-acting reservoir curve until the outer boundary begins to affect the well performance. The figure shows how flow conditions can be divided into infinite-acting, transition, and boundary-dominated cases. Adapted from van Everdingen and Hurst (1949).

- The uppermost, smoothly upward-trending curve reflects infinite-acting or transient conditions caused by the constantly expanding drainage radius.
- The curves that deviate from the infinite-acting reservoir response in each figure define a transition period caused as the reservoir system changes from an infinite-acting to an outer-boundary condition. As would be expected, greater drainage distances would initiate transition flow further along the infinite-acting portion of the curve.
- The essentially flat-lying curve in Fig. 1.7 when the producing rate is completely defined by a closed reservoir system.

All bounded reservoir histories begin and initially follow along the smooth, increasing infinite-acting curve at early time. Each rate curve remains in the infinite-acting condition until the size of the reservoir, as indicated by the r_{eD} ratio, causes the transition from infinite-acting to boundary-dominated flow, where either the producing rate or the flowing bottomhole pressure must change to maintain the shape of the curve.

The expected field rate at any particular time can be determined from the figure for infinite acting or r_{eD} = 2, 4, and 8 reservoirs by incorporating the field permeability, porosity, viscosity, total compressibility, and wellbore radius characteristics into Eq. 1.39 to calculate the appropriate dimensionless time. An equivalent dimensionless flow rate is then interpreted from the appropriate curve. Apply Eq. 1.38 to convert the dimensionless rate value to a field-producing rate.

1.17 Boundary-Dominated Flow Solutions

The following development summarizes the efforts of a number of investigators when developing rate-pressure relationships for closed, circular reservoirs. The discussion touches on the van Everdingen and Hurst (1949) constant-rate solutions to study transient-pressure responses, while more emphasis is placed on the development of the constant-pressure solution to study the exponential rate-time curve.

1.17.1 The Constant-Rate Solution. The equation describing pseudosteady-state pressure drawdown resulting from constant-rate production for a closed-boundary, circular reservoir can be expressed in the following form, which is similar in form to that given by Ramey and Cobb (1971). Note: The majority of the terms on the right side of the equation help describe reservoir volume.

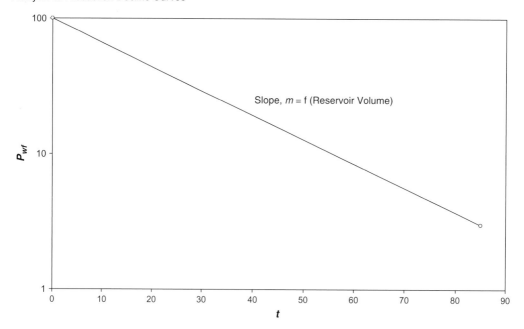

Fig. 1.8—The idealized well-test plot, in which drawdown is a function of time. This figure is similar to the reservoir-limits plot.

$$\frac{kh\left(p_i - p_{wf}\right)}{141.2q\mu B} = \frac{2}{\left(r_e / r_w\right)^2}\left(\frac{0.00633kt}{\phi\mu c_t r_w^2}\right) + \left(\ln\frac{r_e}{r_w} - \frac{3}{4} + S\right). \quad \dots\dots\dots\dots\dots\dots\dots (1.42)$$

The equation of a straight line may be applied to the previous equation. **Fig. 1.8** shows an example of the straightline pressure-time plot developed from Eq. 1.42. All terms in the equation may be treated as constants, except for bottomhole-flowing pressure and time. The figure represents the well-known transient-pressure reservoir limit or drawdown test plot. The slope of a bottomhole flowing pressure-time plot reflects the hydrocarbon pore volume for this closed-reservoir case.

1.17.2 The Constant-Pressure Solution. Fetkovich expressed the van Everdingen-Hurst constant-pressure solution to the diffusivity equation for a closed, circular reservoir in the form of an exponential equation (Fetkovich et al. 1987; Fetkovich 1980). This solution was developed from Fetkovich (1971) to create a method to calculate water influx in closed aquifers.

The exponential decline curve reflects semicompressible liquid production from a closed reservoir. The slope of the decline curve is influenced by reservoir volume and the constancy of the compressibility and bottomhole-flowing pressure. This observation was initially mentioned by Arps (1956) and Brons (1963). The idea was theoretically verified by Fetkovich (1971), who showed that the solution to the diffusivity equation for constant-pressure, boundary-dominated depletion conditions is the same as the Arps (1956) equation for an exponential decline curve.

The rate-transient solution for a closed, circular reservoir for the constant, bottomhole-flowing pressure case can be converted to an exponential form as follows:

$$q = \frac{kh\left(p_i - p_{wf}\right)}{141.2\mu B\left[\ln\left(\frac{r_e}{r_w}\right) - \frac{3}{4} + S\right]}\exp\left\{\left(\frac{0.00633kt}{\phi\mu c_t r_w^2}\right)\frac{-2}{\left(\frac{r_e}{r_w}\right)^2\left[\ln\left(\frac{r_e}{r_w}\right) - \frac{3}{4} + S\right]}\right\}. \quad \dots\dots\dots\dots (1.43)$$

Taking the logarithm of both sides and applying the equation of a straight line to Eq. 1.43 results in Eq. 1.44. Note: All the terms, except for rate and time, can (for most cases) be assumed to remain constant.

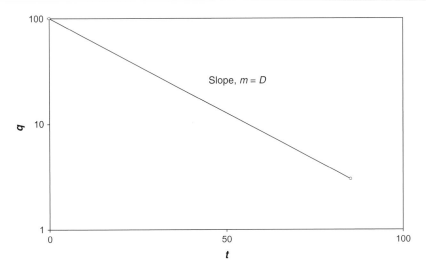

Fig. 1.9—Solution to the diffusivity equation for a well producing a single-phase, slightly compressible fluid at a constant bottomhole-flowing pressure from a bounded reservoir.

$$\ln q = \ln\left\{\frac{kh\left(p_i - p_{wf}\right)}{141.2\mu B\left[\ln\left(\frac{r_e}{r_w}\right) - \frac{3}{4} + S\right]}\right\} - \left\{\left(\frac{0.00633kt}{\phi\mu c_t r_w^2}\right)\left(\frac{r_e}{r_w}\right)^2\left[\ln\left(\frac{r_e}{r_w}\right) - \frac{3}{4} + S\right]\right\}. \quad \dots\dots\dots (1.44)$$

A straightline figure may be constructed when the logarithm of the rate is plotted on the y axes and time plotted on the x axes. **Fig. 1.9** displays a typical figure of the semilog rate-time plot.

The forms of Eq. 1.44 and the rate-time relationship established for the exponential decline, shown as Eq. 1.11, are exponential in nature. Therefore, an exponential decline curve theoretically represents radial flow of a single-phase, slightly compressible fluid from a bounded, circular, and homogeneous reservoir. An exponential decline should be apparent for all types of closed reservoirs in their final depletion stage.

1.18 Time to Attain Boundary-Dominated Flow

One question that always arises is: How long does it take for the pressure disturbance to reach the outermost limit of the reservoir? The following example calculation illustrates that this occurrence may be much shorter than you would expect.

Craft and Hawkins (1959) showed that the time for a reservoir to begin to be influenced by boundary-dominated flow is a function of the system radius and is inversely proportional to the diffusion constant. This equation is expressed as Eq. 1.45 when the units of permeability are millidarcies.

$$t_{\text{pss}} = \frac{40\phi\mu c_t r_e^2}{k}, \text{ days.} \quad \dots\dots\dots\dots\dots\dots\dots\dots\dots\dots\dots\dots\dots\dots\dots\dots\dots (1.45)$$

Eq. 1.45 was applied to the example reservoir cases shown in **Table 1.3** to illustrate the time required for a pressure disturbance to travel from the wellbore to the outer boundary for a 160-acre oil reservoir and a 640-acre gas reservoir at low and high pressures. Specific reservoir characteristics and results of the calculations are also listed in the table. Pressure disturbance travel time for these three examples ranges from 1.3 days to a little less than 4 days.

These calculations illustrate that boundary-dominated flow is initiated within a matter of a few days for moderate-permeability and moderate-compressibility reservoirs. However, one must remember that Eq. 1.44 is an approximation, and the results of the calculations should be viewed as qualitative.

TABLE 1.3—RESERVOIR CHARACTERISTICS			
	Oil Reservoir	High-Pressure Gas Reservoir	Low-Pressure Gas Reservoir
Viscosity, cp	0.6	0.022	0.018
Porosity, %	12	12	12
Compressibility, 1/psi	20×10^{-6}	40×10^{-6}	170×10^{-6}
Permeability, md	50	10	100
Drainage area, acres	160	640	640
Outer boundary, ft	1,490	2,980	2,980
t_{pss}, days	2.6	3.8	1.3

1.19 Type Curves

The science of decline-curve analysis did not materially move beyond the Arps (1945, 1956) concepts for nearly 50 years until Fetkovich (1980) developed type curves encompassing both transient- and boundary-dominated flow conditions. Type curves express in graphical form predetermined solutions to an equation. The interpreter believes that the field curve solution is the same as the solution to the flow equation when the two curves match. Performance and reservoir characteristics for the field situation are predicted by applying the dimensionless equations relating the type curves to the field data. Unfortunately, type curves possess some limiting characteristics.

The compressing effect of logarithmic scales presents the widest possible range of conditions on a single figure. Diversity in the shapes of the curves and differences between the shapes of adjacent type curves are often subtle. A unique match is often difficult to achieve because the curves may be approximately the same shape.

In some cases, type curves presenting different solutions to the diffusivity equation may look surprisingly similar. One should understand the basic geology, production test, and reservoir boundary conditions when applying type curves to solve a field problem. The uninitiated tend to analyze the data solely in the context of the type-curve interpretation. Remember, "*He who would distinguish the true from the false must have an adequate idea of what is true and false*" (Spinoza). Try and find corroborating evidence to add weight to your interpretation.

1.20 Recent Advances in Decline-Curve Analyses

The coupling of the transient production decline performance of a vertical well (which has a fundamental theoretical basis) with the empirically derived Arps (1945, 1956) boundary-dominated flow-decline behavior stems, such as the composite production decline curves developed by Fetkovich et al. (1987) and Fetkovich (1980) used empirically derived scaling parameters. The scaling parameters required for the ordinate and abscissa axes, so that the transient- and boundary-dominated flow-decline stems could be smoothly coupled, were selected by trial and error until a suitable composite decline behavior could be achieved. Fetkovich et al. (1987) and Fetkovich (1980) demonstrated that, theoretically, the rate-transient solution of the production decline behavior of a well under fully boundary-dominated flow using the selected graphical scaling factors resulted in a single late-time decline stem that corresponded to the Arps (1945, 1956) exponential decline stem ($b = 0$).

Using the pressure-transient approach, Doublet and Blasingame (1995a) demonstrated that the boundary-dominated production decline behavior of a well under pseudosteady-state flow conditions corresponded to an Arps (1945, 1956) harmonic decline ($b = 1$). A significant contribution of the Doublet and Blasingame (1995a) work was that it also demonstrated that a theoretical basis could be established for coupling the transient and boundary-dominated flow-production performance behavior of an unfractured vertical well using the corresponding pseudosteady-state analytic pressure-transient solution. The application of this general technique has also been used in the development of composite-production decline curves of other well types in closed, bounded reservoirs, such as for vertically fractured and horizontal wells (Doublet and Blasingame 1995a; Doublet et al. 1994; Shih and Blasingame 1995). Boundary-dominated flow rate-transient solutions can also be used to derive composite decline-curve ordinate and abscissa scaling factors that are identical to those obtained using the pressure-transient solution approach followed by Doublet and Blasingame (1995a).

Palacio and Blasingame (1993) demonstrated that the use of an approximate production-time plotting function (analogous to the Horner approximation of the pseudoproducing time) derived from the production performance of a well could be used to correlate a varying flow rate production history of a well with production decline-curve solutions developed assuming a constant well flow rate. The pseudosteady-state flow time function employed by Crafton (1997) for boundary-dominated flow-production performance evaluation is identical to the production time function approximation employed by Palacio and Blasingame (1993), which was derived specifically for pseudosteady-state flow conditions.

The techniques developed by Doublet and Blasingame (1995a) and Palacio and Blasingame (1993) were later used by Agarwal et al. (1999) to develop a production performance analysis methodology involving a combination of decline curve and specialized pseudosteady-state-flow graphical analyses. Limitations concerning the use of the time function approximation used in the Palacio and Blasingame (1993) and Agarwal et al. (1999) analyses were later identified and reported in the literature (Poe and Marhaendrajana 2002).

In addition, a common problem encountered when performing a production decline analysis of the performance of producing wells is that the production history record (i.e., flowing pressures and flow rates) is often incomplete, or portions of the data may be incomplete or missing entirely. A production decline-curve analysis technique for evaluating the performance of a well with an incomplete or absent wellbore-flowing pressure history has been presented by Poe (2002), in which a hybrid form of the Horner approximation of the pseudoproducing time and superposition-in-time functions can be used. This technique involves correction of the Horner approximation of the pseudoproducing time function used by Palacio and Blasingame (1993), with the dimensionless pseudoproducing time function derived using the rate-transient solution for the well and reservoir type of interest. Limitations of the methodology are related to decline-matching uniqueness issues, and it is preferred that if the actual wellbore-flowing pressure history is available in addition to the flow rates, greater accuracy and uniqueness can be obtained using both decline-curve and specialized graphical analyses.

Many recent advances in production decline-curve analyses presented in this discussion are relatively new and may not have been subjected to a thorough peer review of the literature and concepts used. In some cases, the development work reported in the literature lacks the necessary clarity or completeness, even though these developments have a sound theoretical basis and have been adopted and incorporated into many of the commercially available production decline-curve analysis software models currently available. These advances in production decline-curve analysis have proved to be very useful in characterizing the production performance of a wide variety of well and completion types in practice, and it is therefore important that this technology be addressed and included in a textbook on current production decline-curve analysis practices. It is therefore the intent of Chapter 8 to provide a synthesis of the recent literature on this subject, thereby providing the necessary clarity and consistency for the application and use of this production decline-curve-analysis technology.

Chapter 2

Application of Decline Curves

Decline-curve analysis is often dismissed as a qualitative exercise, because fitting an equation to a production curve does not provide a particularly reasoned basis for predicting performance. This reasoning goes on to state that generally, production data are often of poor quality. Applying these data to determine the equation of a line can result in a really bad interpretation. However, knowledge of the assumptions underlying decline-curve analysis fundamentals coupled with some idea of the field- or reservoir-producing characteristics can provide a sound basis when predicting future characteristics. Also, production data for most cases are not all that inconsistent over reasonable periods of time; however, there are always exceptions to the rule.

The following sections discuss the assumptions forming the basis for applying the Arps (1945) decline-curve methodology and present examples of the effects of different operating and depletion mechanisms on decline-curve shapes.

2.1 Assumptions

Arps (1945, 1956) stated that an exponential decline results when the produced fluid is slightly compressible, the reservoir is a closed system, and the well is producing at a constant bottomhole flowing pressure (BHFP). In other words, the sum of the energies helping to produce the oil or gas changes in a uniform manner. The addition of new energy sources, such as increasing gas saturations, gas expansion effects at lower pressures, latent water influx, layering, or changes in the producing rate, can alter the original depletion mechanism.

Reservoir pressure is proportional to the remaining oil and gas measured at stock-tank conditions for a closed, constant compressibility system. This statement is only true for depletion-type oil reservoirs operating near their bubblepoint and high-pressure gas reservoirs. Dramatic changes in compressibility and effective permeability can cause the curve to become hyperbolic (Brons 1963). The productivity index remains constant throughout the life of a well for this case. A constant productivity index implies that the producing rate is proportional to the reservoir pressure. The same condition applies to a gas well with a constant absolute open flow absolute open flow (AOF) potential.

The Arps decline curves should not be applied to study early-time production data obtained from low-permeability, layered, and/or naturally fractured reservoirs, because the inflow at the sandface remains in an unstable condition for an extended period of time. The curve may exhibit values that result in quite incorrect reserves estimates if practical limits are not applied to the prediction. Some knowledge of the basic geology, reservoir fluid composition, and general producing character is a prerequisite for conducting an intelligent decline-curve study.

Some of the basic assumptions forming the basis for applying the Arps decline-curve equations to analyze reservoir behavior are discussed in the following subsections.

2.1.1 Constant Operating Conditions. **Fig. 2.1** shows how different flow rates affect the decline curve of a California field (Allen 1931). The uppermost lines represent periods of unrestricted flow, while the lower lines represent the effects of choking the well back during times of field proration. Mechanically restricting flow in the production string increases the BHFP and changes the operating conditions.

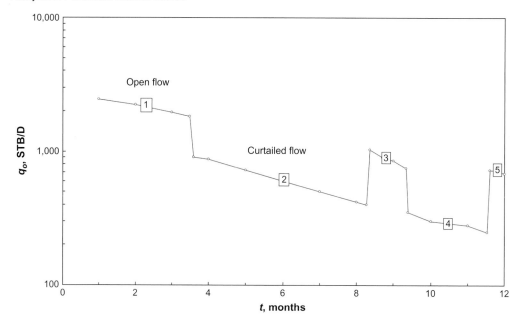

Fig. 2.1—The effect of changing the choke size on the production decline curve. Increasing back pressure reduces pressure drop across the reservoir—hence, the producing rate is also reduced. Note: The slopes of the lines stay approximately the same. Adapted from Allen (1931).

The producing history is divided into five producing segments. The figure shows how well or property histories can be segmented into periods of constancy of operating conditions. Remember: Performance predictions are predicated on an assumed constancy of future operating conditions.

2.1.2 Absence of Mechanical Restrictions. Production may often occur without any flow restriction. Wells producing by artificial lift are usually assumed to be operating with unrestricted flow. This statement is not always true, but for most cases it is a valid assumption. Choking back a well induces an artificial flow restriction.

Fig. 2.2 is an example of an Ellenberger gas well located in the Gomez field (Huddleston 1991). The semi-log rate-time plot for the first 10 years of history displays a well-defined exponential decline. Future performance can be predicted with an apparent high degree of certainty. However, pipeline capacity restraint caused the well to be choked back and produced at a higher backpressure after 9.4 years of essentially unrestricted flow. There is an abrupt change in the slope of the line at the point when the operating conditions were changed. The increased backpressure significantly reduced the reserves estimate.

2.2 The Effects of Reservoir-Depletion Mechanisms

Reservoirs exhibiting the following characteristics are amenable to any type of curve-fitting process. The candidates are reservoirs suffering a measurable loss in reservoir pressure; gravity-drainage reservoirs; and reservoirs exhibiting a gradually increasing water cut or producing gas/oil ratio (GOR).

The last reservoir type occurs when the loss in the primary product, oil or gas, is caused by the intrusion of a constantly increasing volume of some outside source fluid. In the case of an oil well, the intrusion can come from an expanding overlying gas cap and/or an underlying water leg. Gas wells often show increasing water production, which interjects a second producing fluid into the wellstream.

In many cases, the volume of the unwanted fluid in the wellstream may increase over a number of years. In any case, there is a smoothly changing production curve from which a trend into the future can be interpreted. Increasing water volumes increase the hydrostatic head, which artificially increases the apparent backpressure. This effect tends to reduce the producing rate of the primary producing fluid. Prediction methods applicable to this last case are discussed in Chapter 7.

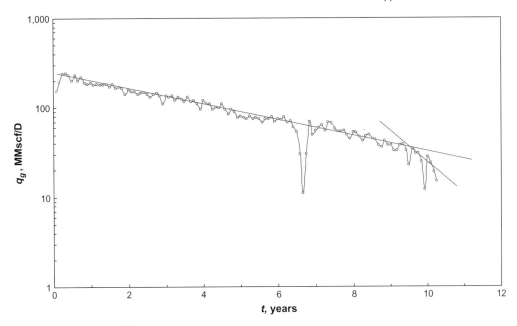

Fig. 2.2—A double exponential decline of an Ellenberger gas well caused by increased backpressure at 9.4 years. What would happen to the curve if the backpressure were reduced? Adapted from Huddleston (1991).

2.2.1 Likely Reservoir Candidates. Pressure-depleting and gravity-drainage oil reservoirs lend themselves to decline-curve analysis, because the constantly declining pressure differential between the static reservoir and BHFP controls the producing rate. Muskat (1949) discussed the Florence field as an example of a solution-gas-drive oil reservoir. **Fig. 2.3** illustrates the rather smoothly declining 25-year history of Wells 85 and 86. Curve fits can be achieved through either decline history of the two wells. Gravity drainage reservoirs display similar characteristics.

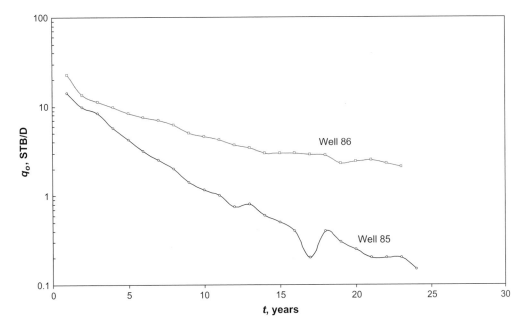

Fig. 2.3—Two well-defined production decline curves from the Florence field. Adapted from Muskat (1949).

2.2.2 Poor Reservoir Candidates. Encroaching water or gas can replace the majority of the produced reservoir fluids. Therefore, there is little pressure or production loss until a secondary fluid (i.e., water or gas) enters the wellstream. **Fig. 2.4** is an example of an 11,000-ft-deep gas well in the Atchafalaya Bay field (Huddleston 1991). The gas-producing rate and the water/gas ratio remain stable for approximately 34 months. Extrapolation of the obvious straight line into the future would cause the reserves to be overestimated. Repressurization effects of the efficient waterdrive maintained reservoir pressure. The AOF potential of the well did not change significantly with these constant conditions, and water production did not increase until the very end. The decline in the gas-producing rate between Months 34 and 49 was caused by the well gradually loading up with water. The gradually increasing hydrostatic head increases the BHFP, thus inducing additional backpressure at the perforations.

2.2.3 Knowledge of General Field Character. Knowledge of reservoir rock type and fluid as well as the expected drive mechanism would be a considerable aid when interpreting a decline curve. The mathematical extension of the past producing history should be viewed only as an addition to other knowledge that you already possess about the area.

For instance, decline-curve analysis should not be performed on tight reservoirs in the early stages of depletion, unless one understands that transient conditions exclusively control the character of the performance curve. The extended prediction tail occurs only when boundary-dominated flow conditions predominate. Early-time data are a reflection of drainage very close to the wellbore when the apparent reservoir limit is small.

Fig. 2.5 represents the production history of a Dakota well in the Wattenberg field (Huddleston 1991). There is a very steep decline at early time. Extrapolation of this early decline to a minimum rate of 1 MMscf/month indicates that the well can last for only 14 months. In actuality, there was a pronounced change in the slope during the 10- to 15-month period. The second extrapolation indicates that the well should be long lived and produce as long as the EL of the well remains at 1 to 2 MMscf/month and major well work is not required.

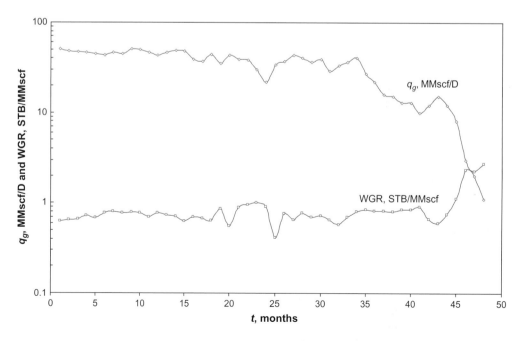

Fig. 2.4—Producing history of a good waterdrive reservoir. The dramatic decline of the gas-producing rate occurred when water production began to increase at 34 months. Extrapolation of the 0- to 36-month straightline fit would have greatly overestimated reserves. Adapted from Huddleston (1991).

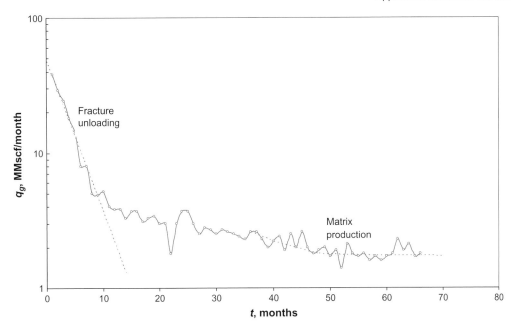

Fig. 2.5—The characteristic double exponential production decline of a dual-porosity well located in the Wattenberg field. Extending the matrix production line into the future could lead to a very optimistic view of the remaining productive potential. Adapted from Huddleston (1991).

The previous figure is an example of a problem that often arises when applying history-matching techniques to predict future character without regard to the reservoir characteristics. The late time-depletion history is completely different from the early-time history. Extending the early-time exponential curve to the EL can result in an unnecessarily pessimistic forecast. Applying the early-time curve cannot be considered if a general knowledge of the nature of dual-porosity reservoirs are coupled with the performance history of the well.

2.2.4 Effects of Adding or Abandoning Wells. Theoretically, performance histories of wells located in the same field or reservoir display similar characteristics when reservoir rock and fluid characteristics are assumed to be uniform. **Fig. 2.6,** adapted from Cutler (1924), represents a plot of well-producing rates for nine tracts located in the Salt Creek field in Wyoming. Incremental production for a particular tract was divided by the number of wells producing from the property to calculate an average per-well producing rate. The results of these efforts are plotted in the figure. Observe the well-defined exponential production decline curve. This curve can be used to predict the expected initial production rate of a new field well, even though the overall decline rate increases because of the additional field outlet. The reasonable straightline fit of the data indicates that the field is probably pressure depleting.

Production decline curves developed on a total field or on a per-well basis do not necessarily present the same picture. **Fig. 2.7** plots the production history calculated on a fieldwide and per-well basis for the 19.6-md Danville (Pettit) field in East Texas (*Occurrence of Oil and Gas in Northeast Texas* 1989). The production history was affected by a combination of pressure-depletion and partial-waterdrive mechanisms and can be divided into three segments. Field production and the rate per well remained essentially constant during Years 3 through 10. Field and per-well production declined at essentially similar rates during Years 14 through 22. Watering out of many of the downdip wells during the period of Years 25 through 29 caused the number of producing wells to decline to 4 from the original field total of 18. The field-producing rate declined dramatically during this time period. On the other hand, the wells remaining higher than the advancing oil/water contact (OWC) continued to produce at an average 3,300 STB/yr.

This example illustrates how the total field-production decline curve probably presents an erroneous view of the reserves potential. A structure map showing the relation of the currently producing wells to the encroaching OWC must be included in the analysis process.

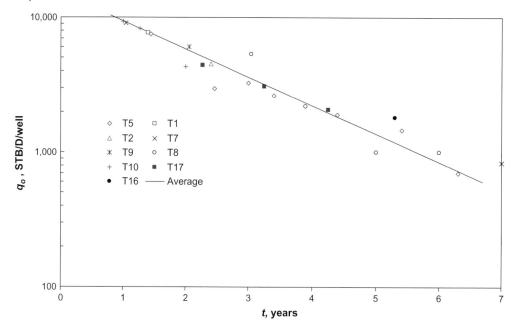

Fig. 2.6—A field type curve developed from the production histories of nine tracts located in the Salt Creek field in Wyoming. Note the increased apparent fluctuation in the data after 4 years. Adapted from Cutler (1924).

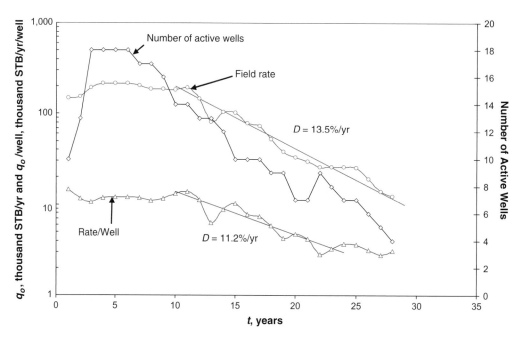

Fig. 2.7—Comparing the total field and per-well producing rates for the Danville (Pettit) field. Production credited on a per-well basis remained constant during the last 6 years even though the field rate continued to decline. Adapted from *Occurrence of Oil and Gas in Northeast Texas* (1989).

Fig. 2.8 shows dissimilar field and per-well production histories for the low-permeability (0.1-md) Trawick (Travis Peak) field located in east Texas. The *Occurrence of Oil and Gas in Northeast Texas* publication (1989) states that the wells are typically fractured with 500,000 to 1 million lbm of sand. A 1.3%/yr or less exponential decline rate is established on the semilog per-well rate plot. The well count declined from 60 to

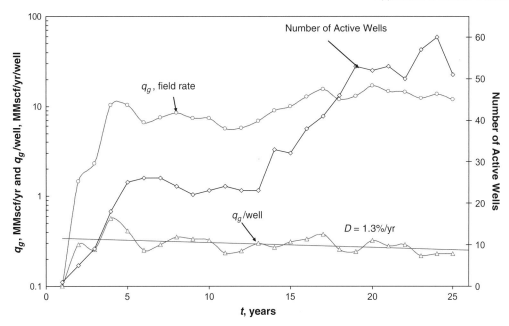

Fig. 2.8—Comparing the total field and per-well producing rates for the very-low-permeability Trawick (Travis Peak) field. Field off-take rate is a function of the number of producing wells. Adapted from *Occurrence of Oil and Gas in Northeast Texas* (1989).

51 wells during the last year, probably because the active-drilling campaign included some marginally successful wells.

The previous discussion indicates that adding or subtracting the number of active-producing wells from a field affects the performance history. A more reliable technique for estimating future production is to analyze performance on a per-well basis.

2.3 Production Segments

Changing operating conditions can alter a well history to such a degree that trends in producing character appear to be indecipherable. These fluctuations preclude any reasonable comparison of the histories of adjacent wells. A series of straightline approximations representing individual correlation segments of oil-producing rate, GOR, and water cut can be drawn for each well history. The highly erratic history is changed to a series of smooth representations. Comparison of adjacent well histories is now possible.

One of the major problems when characterizing a multilayered reservoir is defining interwell drainage boundaries. A fundamental method for evaluating reservoir extent and interwell continuity is to compare producing characteristics of adjacent wells. Similarity of performance histories implies that the wells are completed in similar-quality sands and located in a common reservoir. Performance histories of adjoining wells are plotted in a common figure to compare their characteristics. The following example illustrates this concept.

A study of the remaining potential of the wells completed in the Lisama field in the Middle Magdalena basin in Colombia was conducted by Empressa Colombiana de Petroleos (Ecopetrol)*. The gross producing interval of the field consists of at least 2,000 ft of interbedded sands and shales deposited in an aggrading fluvial depositional environment. Geological studies indicated that the pay sands are lenticular, reservoir extent is limited, and sand quality can change dramatically within a very short, lateral distance. The majority of the field was developed between 1974 and 1980. The heterogeneous field was divided into a number of producing areas exhibiting common characteristics when the segment concept was applied.

---

* Personal communication, courtesy Empresa Colombiana de Petroleos (1992).

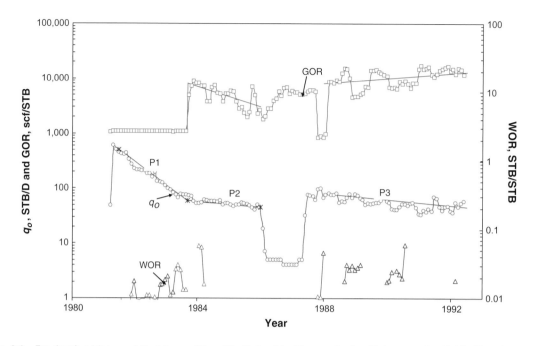

Fig. 2.9—Production history of the Lisama 95 well in Colombia. The producing history can be divided into four obvious producing segments. The 1986 through mid-1987 period was discarded from the analysis process because of the dramatic production loss.

Fig. 2.9 presents and compares the field performance and correlation segment history for the L95 well. The 1986 through mid-1987 period is not included as a correlation segment because of the dramatic decrease in the oil-producing rate. Trends in the oil-producing rate and GOR are evident, while there were no measurable changes in the water cut. The smoothing process divided the well history into three periods, shown as straight lines in the figure.

Fig. 2.10 presents a comparison of the oil-producing rate and GOR segments of four adjacent wells completed in a locally updip portion of the field. Water production is insignificant in this area. The L67 through L142 well pair is located downdip of the L91 through L95 well pair, and the sand quality between the L67 through L142 well pair is different. Note: The L142 well was completed several years after the other wells had been producing in this area. The upper curves representing the GOR history verify communication between each well pair. The blank areas are time intervals in which the production history was deemed to be too erratic to permit a reasonable straightline approximation. The higher-than-average oil-production rate of the L142 well is probably caused by completing the well in some previously undeveloped sands in 1989.

The figure can be interpreted only in conjunction with knowledge of the geology of the area. An expanding secondary gas cap is probably present, and the four wells are apparently in hydraulic communication.

2.3.1 Annotating Decline Curves. Annotating the production curve can be a useful tool for illustrating field-operating changes over the life of a property. **Fig. 2.11** presents the production history of a portion of the Healdton field in Oklahoma (Cutler 1924). Annotation of the well abandonments, new drills, and plug-backs adds to the amount of information conveyed by the figure. It is evident that the onset of increasing water production was a harbinger of decreasing oil production. Drilling of Well 42 materially increased the oil-production rate from the field.

2.4 Production Relationships

Well tests include oil-, gas-, and water-production rates, flowing and shut-in pressures, and oil gravity measurements. A plot of these data serves as a reference to analyze past behavior. Perusal of these performance plots helps to develop an understanding of well and reservoir producing characteristics. Performance information may be divided into two categories.

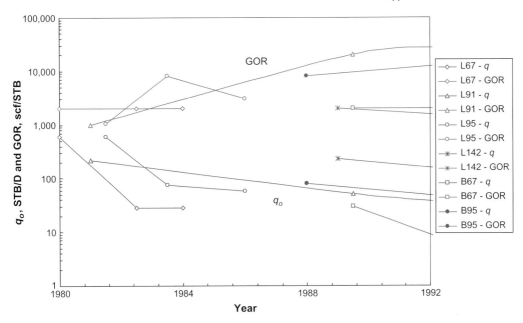

Fig. 2.10—Performance analysis of the Central Basin (CB) completions, central area of the Lisama field. There is an obvious similarity of GOR history for the L91-L95 and L67-L142 well pairs; personal communication (1992).

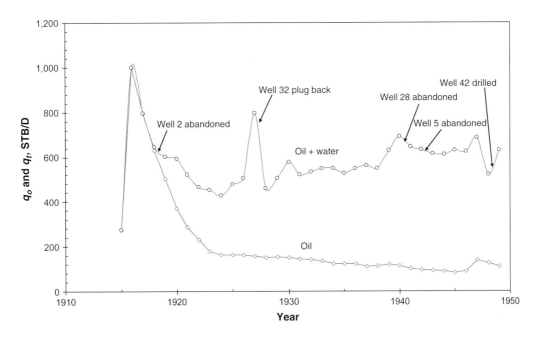

Fig. 2.11—Annotating a field production curve to help explain the history. Note the increasing water production in the field. There was an immediate salutary effect on the field oil rate when Well 42 was drilled. Healdton field, Oklahoma. Adapted from Cutler (1924).

2.4.1 Production Data. Oil-, gas-, and water-production rate measurements are listed in periodic well tests, credited production, or sales ticket files. Unfortunately, water production is often viewed as a nuisance and sometimes is not recorded. An oil-gravity history often provides information about the onset of wellbore communication or the effect of declining reservoir pressure on oil or gas composition.

Plots expressing the rate data in terms of fluid ratios often provide additional insight. Two-phase production from oil wells may be expressed as gas/oil, water/oil, or water-cut ratios. Gas-well production is expressed in liquid/gas relations, such as yield, when relating gas and condensate production or as water cut to express gas/water production relations.

2.4.2 Pressure Data. Flowing tubinghead pressure (FTHP) is a function of flowing bottomhole pressure (FBHP), friction loss, and hydrostatic head. A decreasing FTHP may be caused by the loss of reservoir pressure or an increase in the volume of liquid in the tubing. An increasing GOR in an oil well is generally reflected by an increasing FTHP. Flowing-pressure information is usually included as a part of all well tests.

An analysis of well or reservoir performance is facilitated if all of the production and pressure information is displayed in a single figure. Computer graphics programs permit this type of representation to be easily constructed and updated. **Fig. 2.12** is the partial record of the offshore Texas B-8T well. The modest decrease in the static bottomhole pressure probably indicates the presence of a good waterdrive. The initial solution GOR appears to have been 600 to 700 scf/STB. The marginal change in the reservoir pressure causes the GOR to remain essentially constant, irrespective of periodic fluctuations.

The declining FTHP was probably caused by the increased water production increasing the hydrostatic head in the tubing in early 1963. The FTHP data are not available after 1965 because the well was placed on gas lift. There has been little effect on the oil-producing rate even though there was a significant increase in water production. The cross-sectional area of the completion string was too small to transmit the increased fluid volumes.

The API gravity of the crude did not change significantly. The platform was temporarily shut down in late 1965 for repairs. Dramatic changes in the API gravity often indicate the presence of wellbore communication with other pay sands.

This discussion illustrates the amount of interpreted information available when all performance data are plotted on a single figure. The plot is a pictorial history of the well. Included in this presentation of the well's production history is the static bottomhole pressure (SBHP). The SBHP corresponds to the volumetric average reservoir pore pressure as a function of the reservoir net fluid voidage.

2.5 Mathematical Relationships

A logarithmic scale is equivalent to an exponential equation. The following summarizes the basic algebraic relationships for exponential equations.

The product or quotient of two exponential functions is an exponential outcome term (Purvis 1985, 1987). Eq. 2.1 presents these mathematical relations.

$$\frac{e^x}{e^y} = e^z, \text{ and } e^x \cdot e^y = e^z. \quad\quad\quad (2.1)$$

Subtraction or addition of two exponential functions does not result in an exponential answer. Eq. 2.2 presents these inequalities.

$$e^x \pm e^y \neq e^z. \quad\quad\quad (2.2)$$

Fig. 2.13 shows the production history of the Banff well producing from an undersaturated, moderately viscous oil reservoir depleting by a strong waterdrive (Purvis 1987). The production history may be divided into an increasing water-production segment occurring from Year 0 and a constant water-production segment lasting from Year 3.

Purvis (1987) stated that the water was probably encroaching through a high-permeability stringer. Water production is a function of the total fluid (or oil + water) rate after breakthrough. The oil- and water-producing rates exhibit exponential declines. Therefore, the calculated water/oil ratio (WOR) is a straight line on the semilog plot, because it is the quotient of two exponential expressions. This observation is very useful for predicting future water production rates.

Decline-curve analysis assumes gradually changing reservoir conditions and essentially constant operating conditions. Dramatic changes in operating or reservoir conditions cause erratic production histories that must be divided into a series of smoothed correlation segments to better define the performance characteristics. Interpreting the causes for changes in producing characteristics furnishes the reviewer additional insight into reservoir behavior.

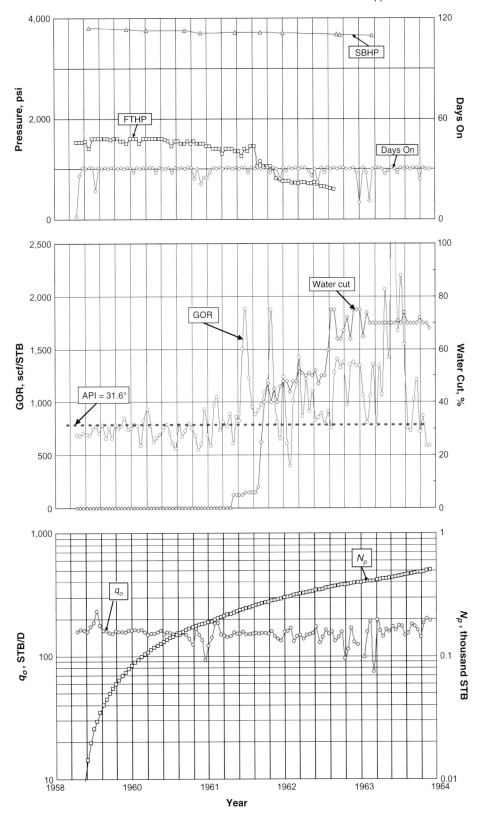

Fig. 2.12—Performance history of the B-8T well, offshore Texas. Marginal loss in reservoir pressure allowed the well-producing rate to remain at a constant level.

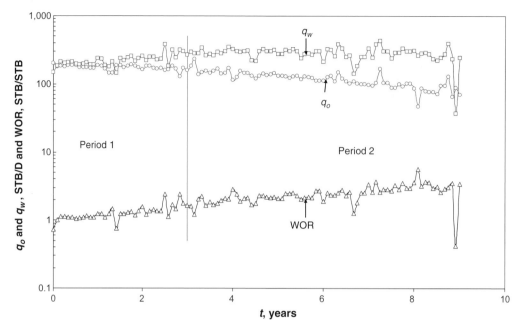

Fig. 2.13—Oil, water, and WOR production history, Banff, Canada, oil well. Adapted from Purvis (1987).

2.6 Statistical Considerations

Production decline histories often appear to be very erratic because of highly variable market conditions, or recurring mechanical or field problems. These variations or noise can be so erratic that the true average curve is difficult to discern. The black line in **Fig. 2.14** illustrates how periodically curtailed gas sales result in a highly variable production history for the Panhandle field well located in Moore County, Texas. The wide variation makes it difficult to interpret a smooth line from the history.

2.6.1 Averaging Production Data. It is often difficult to interpret the best fit of a line through a production decline history because of long- and short-term variations in the raw data. Application of summing or running average equations to the data tends to smooth off short-term peaks and valleys as well as present a more uniform curve.

Line smoothing may appear to increase one's ability to fit a curve to the performance history. However, the smoothing process does not necessarily result in a better quality extrapolation. The production history may be divided into a series of producing segments when long-term changes in operating conditions change the character of the curve.

Campbell (1959) discussed the two methods for smoothing production data. The production rate can be summed over 3 months, 6 months, or a 1-year time period. Additionally, the oscillations within a time unit may be smoothed by summing the previous, subsequent, and actual rate to create an average rate spanning a larger time unit. It should be emphasized that these two methods are statistical in nature. Applications of material balance concepts to these data do not necessarily result in realistic answers. A general summation equation is illustrated in Eq. 2.1.

$$q_t = q_1 + q_2 + q_3 + \dots \qquad (2.3)$$

A three-point, running average calculation smoothes the data by averaging the nth value with the previous and following values. This smoothing method is a standard statistical practice. Stock market statistics are often maintained with 30- and 90-day running averages to smooth out the daily price fluctuations and yet show the trend of the data. Eq. 2.4 expresses a three-point smoothing calculation in terms of producing rate. The nth production-rate point (q_n) and the associated immediately preceding and following production-rate data-point values are used to compute the running average flow rate.

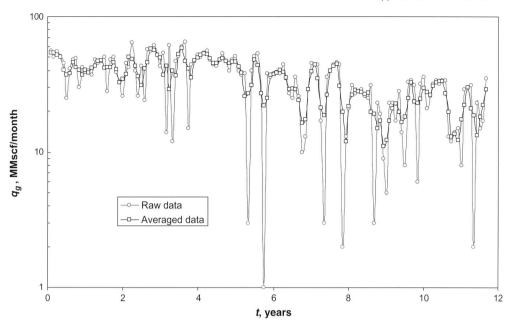

Fig. 2.14—Illustrating effect of smoothing on the production history of a variable rate well. Adapted from Huddleston (1991).

$$q_{\text{avg}} = \frac{q_{n-1} + q_n + q_{n+1}}{3}. \quad\dots\dots\dots\dots\dots\dots\dots\dots\dots\dots\dots\dots\dots\dots\dots\dots\dots (2.4)$$

2.6.2 Problem. The following example problem, plotted in **Fig. 2.15,** compares the three plotting methods. Monthly rate data reflect a well-defined decline even though there is considerable variation in the values.

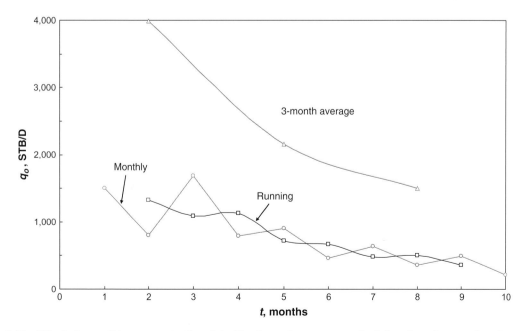

Fig. 2.15—Effect of smoothing on production data. The 3-month-average method disguises the actual performance history. Adapted from Purvis (1985).

Solution. The data were subjected to both the 3-month average and the running average smoothing methods. **Table 2.1** lists the results of these calculations.

Example Calculations.

Sum of 3-month interval = 1,500 + 803 + 1,690 = 3,993 STB/3 months

A 3-month running average = (1,500 + 803 + 1,690)/3 = 1,331 STB/month

Fig. 2.15 shows that the 3-month sum (in blue) method distorts the true decline trend. The distortion is caused by a calculation method that does not maintain a material balance of the reservoir fluids. The running average method results in a smoother curve that also approximates the decline of the raw data. Different averaging methods may present curves for different case studies. In actuality, it is probably best to try working with the raw data, because the smoothing effect can disguise the true decline curve. However, each case is different, and it is hard to make any generalizations about analyzing raw data. Note: Be aware that smoothing may change the character of the performance curve.

Another example of using a 3-month running average to smooth a highly erratic production history has been given previously in Fig. 2.14 at the beginning of this section. The semilog rate-time plot shown in Fig. 2.14 is for Well 29 located in the Panhandle field, Moore County, Texas (Huddleston 1991). The red curve with circles for symbols represents the recorded raw field data. There was obviously a considerable variation in the monthly gas production rate during the last several years of production history. The running average method was used to smooth the data. The running average smoothed curve in the figure (with black squares for symbols) presents the results of these efforts. Smoothing the curve has reduced the "noise." It is apparent that the production history can be divided into three segments. The first segment reflects a gradually increasing rate from 0.5 through 4 years. An obvious decline in the production rate is apparent from 4 through 9 years. The last segment is so erratic that no conclusion can be made concerning the depletion history.

2.6.3 Correcting for Well Downtime. A well is not necessarily operated or produced every day of the month. Production string and surface equipment problems, bad weather, or an inability to sell the gas or oil can cause a well to be temporarily closed in. The actual number of days a well is produced and the total production for the month is always recorded. The producing rate may be calculated by dividing the produced volume by either the number of days the property actually produced or by the number of calendar days. Application of either of the definitions to evaluate a property can result in different pictures of the reservoir character. The following discussion defines the meaning of each of the "calendar day rate" or the "producing day rate" methods.

The calendar day rate is defined as the total production for the month divided by the number of days in the month (or total production for a specified period divided by the time span of interest). The resulting rate value assumes that the production is produced in equal volumes for each time unit comprising the time span. A well is defined to be "underutilized" when it is not produced each day of the time span. The true productive capacity is not reflected by the calendar day rate, because production is allocated not only to the days on production but also to the days when the well was not produced.

Time (months)	Rate (STB/month)	3-Month Average (STB/3 months)	Running Average (STB/month)
		TABLE 2.1—PRODUCTION SCHEDULE: EXAMPLE PROBLEM	
1	1,500	–	–
2	803	3,993	1,331
3	1,690	–	1,095
4	791	–	1,130
5	909	2,160	720
6	460	–	670
7	641	–	488
8	362	1,500	500
9	497	–	358
10	215	–	–

$$\text{Calendar day rate} = \frac{\text{Cumulative production over calendar period}}{\text{Number of days spanning calendar period}}. \quad \dots\dots\dots\dots\dots\dots\dots\dots (2.5)$$

2.6.4 Producing Day Rate. The producing or actual day rate is the total production over a particular time period divided by the number of days the well was actually producing during this interval. This rate reflects the maximum potential if production is not being mechanically curtailed.

$$\text{Producing day rate} = \frac{\text{Cumulative production over the interval}}{\text{Number of days property was produced}} \quad \dots\dots\dots\dots\dots\dots\dots\dots (2.6)$$

The true performance decline can be determined only if the well produces nearly each day of the month. Both the calendar and actual daily production rates are similar in this instance. Unfortunately, a problem arises when production is restricted, and the well is allowed to produce only for a portion of the month. Flow from the sandface into the production string is the endpoint of an orderly progression of fluid movement from the outermost reservoir limits to the wellbore. Fluid afterflow occurs when a well is shut in for any period of time. The apparent production rate when the well is again opened is greater than that observed under normal daily production operations, because afterflow causes reservoir fluids to migrate toward the wellbore during this time of no production. The apparent rate when the well is reopened to production is optimistic when compared to a normal continuous, pumped-off producing rate. The following example problem is an excellent case to illustrate the difference between the calculated calendar and actual rates on the apparent well history.

Example. The Mannville oil well example was used by Purvis (1987) to illustrate the effect of production rate definition on the calculated production history. **Fig. 2.16** represents the number of days per month that the oil well was produced.

Productive capacity was curtailed to approximately 8 days/month for the first 5.25 years of life. Since then, the well has produced nearly every calendar day of the month. Purvis felt that the increasing producing GOR shown in **Fig. 2.17,** coupled with no evidence of significant water production, indicated a pressure-depleting reservoir.

Fig. 2.18 compares the semilog rate-time plot for the calendar and actual daily production rates. Note: The disparity between the results of the calculations during the underutilized period when production averaged only 8 days/month. However, the decline curves are essentially the same during the fully utilized period.

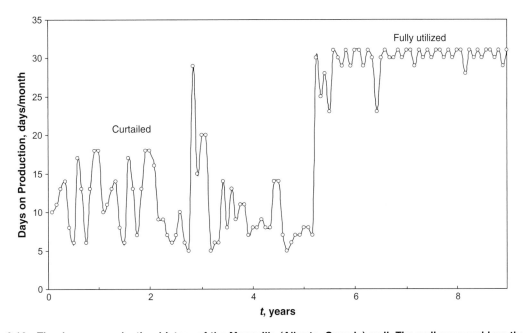

Fig. 2.16—The days-on production history of the Mannville (Alberta, Canada) well. The well averaged less than 8 days/month production for the first 5.4 years. Adapted from Purvis (1987).

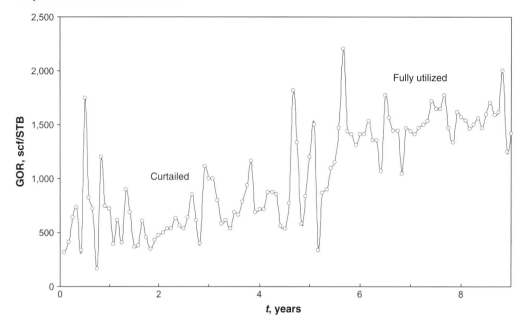

Fig. 2.17—Producing GOR history, Mannville (Alberta, Canada) well. The GOR is seen to significantly increase to a higher GOR during the fully used phase of the well life than that observed during the initial production. Adapted from Purvis (1987).

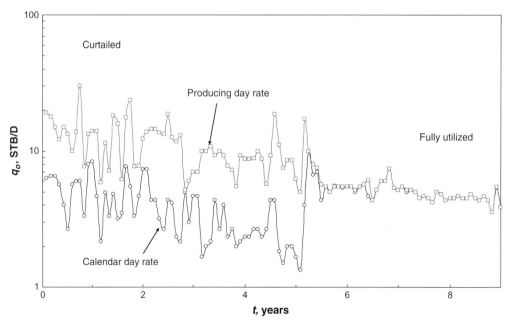

Fig. 2.18—Comparison of the apparent and actual oil-production rates for the Mannville (Alberta, Canada) well. Note the similarity of the calendar and producing day curves when the well is operated in a fully used manner. Adapted from Purvis (1987).

The Mannville well discussed in Figs. 2.16, 2.17, and 2.18 is an example of changing field operations segmenting performance history. The well history was divided into two periods, because the activity changed from an average of 8 days/month production to producing essentially every day in the month. It is evident that the well operated under two different sets of operating conditions. Therefore, the history could have been divided into two segments.

Chapter 3

Type Curves

The type-curve approach matches a curve generated from an equation developed from a specific set of boundary values or conditions, overlaid on a line representing a plot of the field data. For our particular case, the curve shape reflects a production rate decline as a function of time. The combination of conditions representing the type curve and field curve are assumed to be the same if the traces of the two curves are similar (i.e., they overlay each other). Therefore, the solution to the field problem would be solved by inspection as long as the two curves are plotted on the same scale. Extend the field curve outward along the shape of the matched type curve to predict performance. This analysis technique is also used to analyze pressure-time plots to predict performance and determine reservoir characteristics.

Type-curve solutions are presented in logarithmic and dimensionless form to span a wide range of conditions. Mathematical relationships between the dimensionless mathematical curve and the dimensional field curve permit ready translation of the information between the different spaces.

Similar conditions are assumed to prevail for both curves. A word of caution is in order: The analyst assumes that the field and type curves operate under the same assumptions and boundary conditions when a match has been achieved. This is not necessarily true. Often, the quality of the answer is a function of the skill of the interpreter to identify similarity of field- and type-curve boundary conditions. Note: Be sure to understand the field operating conditions before performing an analysis with type curves.

The first part of the following discussion applies the type-curve approach to determine reservoir permeability and wellbore damage for an infinite-acting reservoir flowing with a constant BHFP. However, the Fetkovich (1980) method for analyzing transient data and the Arps curves form the main body of this chapter.

3.1 The Jacob and Lohman Type Curve

Jacob and Lohman (1952) solved the diffusivity equation for a well producing at a constant BHFP in the center of an infinite-acting, homogeneous reservoir. The dimensionless type curve presented in **Fig. 3.1** shows the van Everdingen and Hurst (1949) solution for a constant inner boundary pressure condition shown as Eq. 1.38, with dimensionless time expressed in Eq. 1.39.

The curve is shown in two parts to increase the range of conditions presented in a single figure. Flattening of the rather steep initial slope of the rate curve reflects the gradually increasing drainage volume caused by the expanding outer boundary.

Equations relating field and dimensionless rate-time conditions provide a basis for estimating reservoir permeability and drainage area. The following discussion develops these relationships for the Jacob and Lohman type curves and illustrates the utility of the method.

3.1.1 Fundamental Relationships. Eq. 1.38 represents the van Everdingen and Hurst (1949) dimensionless and field rate relationship for the constant BHFP case rewritten in the form of a ratio of dimensionless to field rates. Field units of flow rate in Eq. 3.1 are stock-tank barrels per day (STB/D).

$$\frac{q_{wD}}{q} = \frac{141.2 B \mu}{kh\left(p_i - p_{wf}\right)}. \qquad \dots\dots\dots\dots\dots\dots\dots\dots\dots\dots\dots\dots\dots\dots\dots\dots\dots\dots\dots\dots\dots (3.1)$$

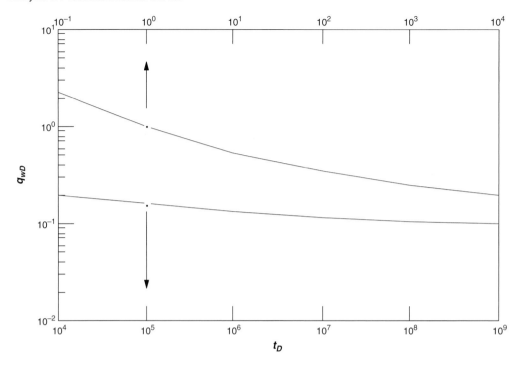

Fig. 3.1—The Jacob and Lohman type curve. As expected, rate loss is more severe at early time. Adapted from Jacob and Lohman (1952).

The numerical difference between the dimensionless and field rate values remains constant, because all the terms on the right side of the equation are assumed to remain constant. Eq. 3.1 reverts to the following form, because the match point ratio term represents the difference between the dimensionless and field values. Any point on the coordinate system may be selected after matching the traces of the type and field curves.

$$\left[\frac{q_{wD}}{q}\right]_{m.p.} = \frac{141.2B\mu}{kh\left(p_i - p_{wf}\right)}. \quad\dots\dots\dots\dots\dots\dots\dots\dots\dots\dots\dots\dots\dots\dots\dots\dots\dots \quad (3.2)$$

Rearrange Eq. 3.2 to solve for permeability.

$$k = \frac{141.2B\mu}{h\left(p_i - p_{wf}\right)}\left[\frac{q}{q_{wD}}\right]_{m.p.}. \quad\dots\dots\dots\dots\dots\dots\dots\dots\dots\dots\dots\dots\dots\dots\dots \quad (3.3)$$

Refer to the van Everdingen and Hurst (1949) dimensionless- and field-time relationship shown as Eq. 1.39. This equation can be expressed in the following form when the units of time are days:

$$\frac{t_D}{t} = \frac{0.00633k}{\phi\mu c_t r_w^2}. \quad\dots\dots\dots\dots\dots\dots\dots\dots\dots\dots\dots\dots\dots\dots\dots\dots\dots\dots \quad (3.4)$$

Eq. 3.4 establishes a ratio relationship between dimensionless and dimensional time when the terms on the right side of the equation are assumed to remain constant. The match point (m.p.) shown in Eq. 3.5 represents the constant value of all the reservoir parameters shown on the right side of the equation.

$$\left[\frac{t_D}{t}\right]_{m.p.} = \frac{0.00633k}{\phi\mu c_t r_w^2}. \quad\dots\dots\dots\dots\dots\dots\dots\dots\dots\dots\dots\dots\dots\dots\dots\dots\dots \quad (3.5)$$

Rearrange Eq. 3.5 to solve for the wellbore radius, r_w. Inserting the apparent wellbore radius term, r_{wa}, in place of the r_w term includes mechanical skin around the wellbore in the equation.

$$r_{wa} = \left[\frac{0.00633k}{\phi \mu c_t} \left(\frac{t}{t_D} \right)_{m.p.} \right]^{0.5}. \quad \dots\dots\dots\dots\dots\dots\dots\dots\dots\dots\dots\dots \quad (3.6)$$

Eq. 3.7 defines the mathematical relationship between the apparent and mechanical wellbore radius as a function of the skin factor, S.

$$S = -\ln \left(\frac{r_{wa}}{r_w} \right). \quad \dots\dots\dots\dots\dots\dots\dots\dots\dots\dots\dots\dots\dots\dots \quad (3.7)$$

3.1.2 Calculation Procedure. Construct a logarithmic rate-time plot of the field data on the same scale as the Jacob and Lohman (1952) type curve to begin the calculation procedure. Obtain a match with the type curve and pick match points. There should be some evidence that the reservoir is infinite-acting, pressure-depleting, and producing at constant BHFP before attempting a match with the Jacob and Lohman type curve, because their curve was founded on these boundary conditions.

Obtain match points if the reservoir permeability and apparent wellbore radius are to be calculated; otherwise, extend the field curve along the type curve to predict performance. Of course, the problem with this method is the extension of production to infinity. One does not encounter this occurrence in real life because of production falloff. **Table 3.1** lists the data requirements for applying the Jacob and Lohman (1952) type-curve approach to calculate permeability and skin.

The following discussion develops the analysis procedure:

Overlay the production decline curve on the type curve. Construct a log-log plot of the field rate-time data on the same scale as the type curve to start the analysis process. Overlay the field curve on the type curve and obtain a match.

Obtain match points. The match points are: q, q_{wD}, t, and t_D. The selection process is easier if the dimensionless points are selected at whole numbers before attempting the match.

Calculate kh or the reservoir permeability. Apply Eq. 3.3 and the reservoir variables listed in Table 3.1 to calculate permeability.

$$k = \frac{141.2 B \mu}{h \left(p_i - p_{wf} \right)} \left[\frac{q}{q_{wD}} \right]_{m.p.}.$$

Calculate the apparent wellbore radius. Apply Eq. 3.6 and the reservoir variables listed in Table 3.1 to calculate the apparent radius.

$$r_{wa} = \left[\frac{0.00633k}{\phi \mu c_t} \left(\frac{t}{t_D} \right)_{m.p.} \right]^{0.5}.$$

Apply Eq. 3.8 to calculate system compressibility as follows:

$$c_t = S_o c_o + S_w c_w + S_g c_g + c_f. \quad \dots\dots\dots\dots\dots\dots\dots\dots\dots\dots\dots\dots \quad (3.8)$$

Oil, gas, and water saturation values are expressed in fractions. In the absence of appropriate data, oil compressibility may be assumed to be $c_o = 30 \times 10^{-6}$ psi^{-1}, and water compressibility $c_w = 3 \times 10^{-6}$ psi^{-1}. Formation

TABLE 3.1—DATA REQUIREMENTS: TRANSIENT TYPE CURVES	
Interval thickness, h (ft)	Wellbore radius, r_w (ft)
System compressibility, c_t (1/psi)	Initial pressure, p_i (psi)
B_o or B_g (RB/STB or RB/scf)	μ_o or μ_g (cp)
BHFP, p_{wf} (psi)	Porosity, ϕ (fraction BV)

TABLE 3.2—M-4x WELL INFORMATION			
h: 30 ft	p_{wf}: 2,660 psi	p_i: 3,360 psi	ϕ : 25 %
c_t: 3×10^{-6} 1/psi	B_o: 1.1 RB/STB	r_w: 0.328 ft	μ_o: 2.3 cp

compressibility c_f usually varies between 3×10^{-6} and 10×10^{-6} psi^{-1}. Use actual field values or the appropriate published correlation if at all possible.

Problem. A 6.7-day, constant BHFP production test was conducted on the M-4x exploration well discussed by Fetkovich et al. (1987). Log and core analysis indicated a moderate permeability producing zone. The well was acidized before testing. Transient conditions were assumed to prevail during the test. Therefore, the Jacob and Lohman (1952) type curve developed for infinite-acting conditions could be used to analyze the production decline. **Table 3.2** lists the reservoir properties and pertinent test conditions.

Calculate reservoir permeability, and determine if the acid treatment affected the apparent wellbore radius. Can you estimate future production characteristics?

Solution. **Fig. 3.2** presents the log-log rate-time plot of the production test and the match with the Jacob and Lohman (1952) type curve.

Overlay and match the field and type curves, and select match points. Remember, the data plotted on log-log paper are the same scale as the Jacob and Lohman (1952) type curve. For simplicity, the match point was chosen on the dimensionless curves as $q_{wD} = 1.0$, $t_D = 10$.

Record the four match points. Remember: These match points represent the difference between the dimensionless and dimensional rate-time relationships and may be obtained at any point on the overlay.

Match points: $q = 2,700$ STB/D, $t = 10.0$ hours, $q_{wD} = 1.0$, $t_D = 10$

Calculate permeability. Apply the reservoir variables listed in Table 3.2 and Eq. 3.3 to calculate the reservoir permeability.

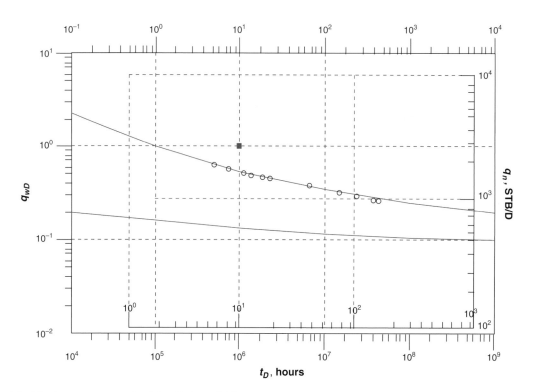

Fig. 3.2—The type-curve match of the M-4x well. The solid line is the type curve, while the symbols are the field data. The single square on the type curve locates the match point chosen in this instance.

$$k = \frac{141.2 B\mu}{h\left(p_i - p_{wf}\right)}\left[\frac{q}{q_{wD}}\right]_{m.p.} = \frac{141.2\left(2.3\right)\left(1.1\right)}{30\left(3,360 - 2,660\right)}\left[\frac{2,700}{1.0}\right]_{m.p.} = 45.9 \text{ md.}$$

Calculate the apparent wellbore radius. The time units for the relatively short production test were hours. These values are converted to units of days, which were the proper units for Eq. 3.6.

$$r_{wa} = \left[\frac{0.00633k}{\phi\mu c_t}\left(\frac{t}{t_D}\right)_{m.p.}\right]^{0.5} = \left[\frac{0.00633\left(45.9\right)}{0.25\left(2.3\right)\left(3\times 10^{-6}\right)}\left[\frac{10}{24\left(10\right)}\right]_{m.p.}\right]^{0.5} = 83.8 \text{ ft.}$$

Apply Eq. 3.7 to calculate the skin effect value. The negative skin indicates the acid job had evidently cleaned up some near-wellbore formation damage.

$$S = -\ln\left(\frac{r_{wa}}{r_w}\right) = -\ln\left(\frac{83.8}{0.328}\right) = -5.5.$$

Estimate future production. Future producing rates are estimated by extending the test data along the type curve and reading the rate values at selected times. However, one should be concerned about extrapolating the infinite-acting solution too far out into the future. In this particular case, Fetkovich (1980) assumed a 640-acre drainage area and used the equation of the area of a circle to calculate the time for the pressure disturbance to migrate out to the 2,980-ft radius.

The preceding example problem applies the type-curve approach to analyze a short-term production test. Permeability, skin, and possibly future production rate are determined. The answers are founded on the assumption that the reservoir is infinite-acting, and the BHFP remains constant during the test period. The Jacob and Lohman (1952) type curves are only applicable for these conditions.

The following discussion extends the type-curve approach to include both the infinite-acting and boundary-dominated conditions.

3.2 The Fetkovich Type Curves

The type-curve-analysis approach is particularly useful for analyzing extended producing histories. Fetkovich (1980) combined solutions to the diffusivity and Arps (1945) equations to provide a more general analysis method for covering a wide range of conditions. Solutions of Tsarevich and Kuranov (1966) and Ferris et al. (1962) for a slightly compressible fluid producing from a homogeneous reservoir with a constant BHFP for infinite-acting and boundary-dominated flow conditions were combined into a single form. The plotting variables for these solutions were the van Everdingen and Hurst (1949) dimensionless rate (Eq. 1.38) and dimensionless time (Eq. 1.39) terms. Various reservoir sizes defined by the van Everdingen and Hurst outer-to-inner reservoir size expression shown as Eq. 1.40 were included to relate the effect of reservoir size on the rate-time response.

Fig. 3.3, developed and discussed by Fetkovich and Thrasher (1979), Fetkovich (1980), and Fetkovich et al. (1987), presents a set of dimensionless rate-time decline curves operating over infinite-acting and boundary-dominated flow regimes. The flat-lying curve reflects transient or infinite-acting conditions, while reservoir size determines the onset of boundary-dominated or pseudosteady-state flow conditions. There is a pronounced decrease in the production rate after an expanding pressure wave encounters the outer boundary. The r_{eD} stems bend away from the infinite-acting curve in relation to reservoir size. These curves show how reservoir size controls the length of time that flow conditions remain in the transient condition. This figure is similar in nature to the water influx solutions presented by van Everdingen and Hurst (1949).

Two important characteristics should be noted about this figure.

- Infinite-acting conditions exist for all stems up to $t_D = 20$.
- A field- and type-curve solution procedure can be applied to predict future performance if there is sufficient bend in field performance data to indicate the presence of boundary-dominated flow.

Fetkovich (1980) redefined the van Everdingen and Hurst (1949) dimensionless variables to transform the curve illustrated in Fig. 3.3 to a new coordinate system. Both transient- and boundary-dominated depletion

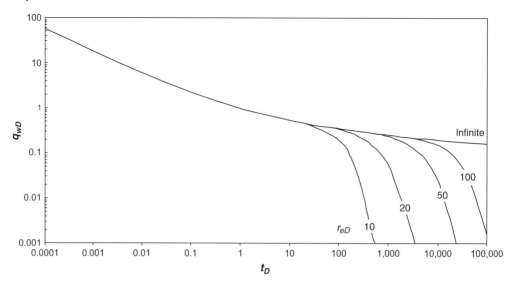

Fig. 3.3—Infinite and finite outer-boundary solutions for a constant bottomhole pressure in a circular reservoir. Each stem can be divided into transient, transition, and completely boundary-dominated sections. Adapted from Fetkovich (1980).

conditions, as well as the empirical Arps (1945) curves, are represented in a single figure. The diffusivity equation defines the transient side of the Fetkovich type curve, while the empirically developed Arps curves define the boundary-dominated conditions. The exponential curve is common to both definitions.

The operational definition of slightly compressible fluids may be translated to the study of low-to-moderate-GOR oil wells or to high-pressure gas wells. The Carter (1985) type-curve approach was proposed to study variable-compressibility systems. For most cases, the practical utility of this concept does not provide any incremental advantage over the Fetkovich (1980) method.

3.2.1 Fundamental Relationships. Fetkovich (1980) coupled the infinite-acting to boundary-dominated rate-time curves and the Arps (1945) empirical decline curves into the same coordinate system. The dimensionless rate and time variables defined in Chapter 1 form the basis for coupling the solutions to the diffusivity equation with the empirically derived Arps curves. These expressions (Eqs. 1.31 and 1.32) are presented in this discussion for completeness.

The dimensionless rate variable (Eq. 1.31) is as follows:

$$q_{Dd} = \frac{q_2}{q_i}.$$

The dimensionless time variable (Eq. 1.32) is as follows:

$$t_{Dd} = D_i t.$$

The first part of the following discussion illustrates how the solution to the diffusivity equation curves are rearranged to the new coordinate system, while the second part deals with rearranging the Arps (1945) curves to the same system.

3.2.2 The Rate Solution for Transient Curves. The numerical solution to the radial flow diffusivity equation for the constant bottomhole pressure production case under infinite-acting, transition, and boundary-dominated flow-depletion conditions was presented previously in Figs. 1.6 and 1.7. The analytic solution for the boundary-dominated flow behavior of an unfractured vertical well can be expressed in dimensionless form as given in Eq. 3.9.

$$q_{wD} = \frac{1}{\left(\ln r_{eD} - \frac{3}{4} \right)} \exp \left[\frac{-2t_D}{r_{eD}{}^2 \left(\ln r_{eD} - \frac{3}{4} \right)} \right]. \quad \dots \dots \dots \dots \dots \dots \dots \dots \dots \dots \quad (3.9)$$

Fetkovich et al. (1987) changed the ¾ value to ½ to provide a better fit between the theoretical and simulated solutions. Including definitions for dimensionless time and radius transforms the previous equation to Eq. 3.10 as follows:

$$q_{wD} = \frac{q}{q_i} \left[\ln \left(\frac{r_e}{r_{wa}} \right) - \frac{1}{2} \right]^{-1}. \quad \dots \dots \dots \dots \dots \dots \dots \dots \dots \dots \dots \dots \dots \quad (3.10)$$

Including the dimensionless rate definition (Eq. 1.31) in the previous equation results in Eq. 3.11 as follows:

$$q_{Dd} = \frac{q}{q_i} = q_{wD} \left[\ln \left(\frac{r_e}{r_{wa}} \right) - \frac{1}{2} \right]. \quad \dots \dots \dots \dots \dots \dots \dots \dots \dots \dots \quad (3.11)$$

Eq. 3.11 establishes a relationship between real time, the dimensionless van Everdingen and Hurst (1949) flow rate, and the dimensionless Fetkovich et al. (1987) decline flow rate definitions. Including the van Everdingen and Hurst (1949) constant pressure solution dimensionless flow rate (Eq. 1.38) with Eq. 3.11 results in a definition of the dimensionless decline flow rate that can be used in the analysis of well-production performance data. This expression is given in Eq. 3.12 as follows:

$$q_{Dd} = \frac{141.2qB\mu}{kh \left(p_i - p_{wf} \right)} \left[\ln \left(\frac{r_e}{r_{wa}} \right) - \frac{1}{2} \right]. \quad \dots \dots \dots \dots \dots \dots \dots \dots \dots \quad (3.12)$$

Taking the logarithm of both sides of Eq. 3.12 results in the following:

$$\ln q_{Dd} = \ln \left[\frac{141.2qB\mu}{kh \left(p_i - p_{wf} \right)} \right] + \ln \left[\ln \left(\frac{r_e}{r_{wa}} \right) - \frac{1}{2} \right]. \quad \dots \dots \dots \dots \dots \quad (3.13)$$

The previous equation establishes a relationship between the Fetkovich et al. (1987) dimensionless rate and the field rate. The difference between the two expressions is the constant (last) term on the right side of Eq. 3.13.

$$\ln \left[\ln \left(\frac{r_e}{r_{wa}} \right) - \frac{1}{2} \right].$$

Eq. 3.12 may be rearranged and used in a decline-curve graphical-matching procedure to solve for the permeability-thickness (formation conductivity) of an oil well. The flow rate units in this expression are given in STB/D.

$$kh = \frac{141.2B\mu}{p_i - p_{wf}} \left[\ln \left(\frac{r_e}{r_{wa}} \right) - \frac{1}{2} \right] \left[\frac{q}{q_{Dd}} \right]_{m.p.}. \quad \dots \dots \dots \dots \dots \dots \dots \quad (3.14)$$

Similar expressions can be developed for estimating the formation conductivity using a gas reservoir decline-curve analysis. The gas flow rate has units of Mscf/D in these expressions. These relationships are presented in Eqs. 3.15 and 3.16. Eq. 3.15 is expressed in terms of the real gas pseudopressure and is generally applicable for all pressure ranges of interest. A more commonly used relationship, expressed in terms of pressure squared, is presented in Eq. 3.16 and is applicable for relatively low-pressure levels, typically pressures of approximately 3,000 psi or less.

$$kh = \frac{1,422T}{p_p \left(p_i \right) - p_p \left(p_{wf} \right)} \left[\ln \left(\frac{r_e}{r_{wa}} \right) - \frac{1}{2} \right] \left[\frac{q}{q_{Dd}} \right]_{m.p.}. \quad \dots \dots \dots \dots \dots \quad (3.15)$$

$$kh = \frac{1,422 T \mu z}{\left(p_i^2 - p_{wf}^2\right)} \left[\ln\left(\frac{r_e}{r_{wa}}\right) - \frac{1}{2}\right]\left[\frac{q}{q_{Dd}}\right]_{m.p.} . \qquad (3.16)$$

Fetkovich (1971) combined the material balance equation with the productivity index equation to develop a method to calculate water influx. One of the relationships developed in his paper is as follows:

$$q = q_i \exp\left(\frac{-q_{i(max)} t}{N_{pi}}\right). \qquad (3.17)$$

This equation looks suspiciously like the Arps (1945) exponential rate equation. In this case, define the initial decline rate as follows:

$$D_i = \frac{q_{i(max)}}{N_{pi}}. \qquad (3.18)$$

The equation is a function of the theoretical maximum production rate and the original oil in place (OOIP) that occurs when $p_{wf} = 0$ for the first case and $q = 0$ for the second case. Eqs. 3.19 and 3.20 define these two maximizing terms. Note that the oil viscosity (μ_{oi}) and formation volume factor (B_{oi}) at intial reservoir conditions are used in the definition of the maximum production rate and original oil in place.

$$q_{i(max)} = \frac{khp_i}{141.2 \mu_{oi} B_{oi} \left[\ln\left(\frac{r_e}{r_w}\right) - \frac{1}{2}\right]}. \qquad (3.19)$$

$$N_{pi} = \frac{\pi\left(r_e^2 - r_w^2\right)\phi c_t hp_i}{5.615 B_{oi}}. \qquad (3.20)$$

Combining these definitions with the field, the Fetkovich et al. (1987) dimensionless and van Everdingen and Hurst (1949) dimensionless time terms result in the following equation:

$$t_{Dd} = \frac{0.00633 kt}{\phi \mu c_t r_{wa}^2} \frac{1}{\frac{1}{2}\left[\left(\frac{r_e}{r_{wa}}\right)^2 - 1\right]\left[\ln\left(\frac{r_e}{r_{wa}}\right) - \frac{1}{2}\right]}. \qquad (3.21)$$

A relationship between the Fetkovich definition of dimensionless time and real time has been established. The terms differ by the following constant term:

$$\frac{1}{\frac{1}{2}\left[\left(\frac{r_e}{r_{wa}}\right)^2 - 1\right]\left[\ln\left(\frac{r_e}{r_{wa}}\right) - \frac{1}{2}\right]}.$$

An expression for estimating the volume of an oilwell drainage area is developed by rearranging Eq. 3.20, substituting the definition for reservoir pore volume, and expressing the answer in reservoir barrels (res bbl):

$$V_p = \frac{\pi\left(r_e^2 - r_{wa}^2\right)\phi h}{5.615} = \left[\frac{\bar{B}_o \bar{\mu}_o}{\mu_{oi}\bar{c}_t\left(p_i - p_{wf}\right)}\right]\left[\frac{t}{t_{Dd}}\right]_{m.p.}\left[\frac{q}{q_{Dd}}\right]_{m.p.} . \qquad (3.22)$$

A similar expression for estimating the pore volume of a gas reservoir from production decline performance matching is given in Eq. 3.23, in which the pore volume units used are expressed in reservoir cubic feet (rcf). In low-pressure reservoirs (3,000 psia or less), the pressure-squared approximation of the real gas pseudo-pressure function is applicable, and an alternate relationship for estimating the reservoir pore volume can be used, given by Eq. 3.24.

$$V_p = \pi \left(r_e^2 - r_{wa}^2 \right) \phi h = \left[\frac{56.557T}{\mu_{gi} \bar{c}_t \left(p_p \left(p_i \right) - p_p \left(p_{wf} \right) \right)} \right] \left[\frac{t}{t_{Dd}} \right]_{m.p.} \left[\frac{q}{q_{Dd}} \right]_{m.p.} \quad \dots \dots \dots \dots \dots \quad (3.23)$$

$$V_p = \pi \left(r_e^2 - r_{wa}^2 \right) \phi h = \left[\frac{56.557T \bar{\mu}_g \bar{z}}{\mu_{gi} \bar{c}_t \left(p_i^2 - p_{wf}^2 \right)} \right] \left[\frac{t}{t_{Dd}} \right]_{m.p.} \left[\frac{q}{q_{Dd}} \right]_{m.p.} \quad \dots \dots \dots \dots \dots \quad (3.24)$$

For most cases, the viscosity values in Eq. 3.22 through 3.24 in the numerator and denominator are assumed similar and therefore cancel out. Any differences between initial and current viscosity are generally rendered negligible by the greater inherent inaccuracies of the curve match or the system compressibility estimate. Therefore, this variable is usually neglected.

The formation volume factor is evaluated at the pressure midway between initial pressures and BHFPs. However, it is normally assumed to be equal to the initial formation volume factor. This assumption may be reasonable for the majority of black-oil and high-pressure-gas reservoir cases, but may introduce an additional inaccuracy for moderate-to-low-pressure gas reservoirs because of the compressibility of gas at these pressures. Care should be exercised when selecting the proper fluid properties for gas reservoirs operating with a large-pressure drawdown and for pressure-depleting, high-GOR (HGOR) oil wells.

The type-curve stem selected from the match with the field data defines the r_e/r_{wa} value. Eq. 3.21 can be rewritten to obtain a form that can be used to determine the apparent wellbore radius (for either an oil or gas reservoir) after the type-curve stem (with associated $[r_{eD}]_{m.p.}$) has been selected.

$$r_{wa} = \left[\frac{0.0127k}{\phi \mu c_t \left[\left(r_{eD} \right)_{m.p.}^2 - 1 \right] \left[\ln(r_{eD})_{m.p.} - \frac{1}{2} \right]} \left[\frac{t}{t_{Dd}} \right]_{m.p.} \right]^{0.5} \quad \dots \dots \dots \dots \dots \quad (3.25)$$

This value of apparent wellbore radius obtained with the solution of Eq. 3.25 can be combined with Eq. 3.7 to calculate the relation between the apparent and mechanical wellbore radius, in terms of the skin factor.

Fig. 3.4 presents the Fetkovich transformation of the Fig. 3.3 log-log, rate-time plot to the new coordinate system. The correlation stems are of the same character as those developed by van Everdingen and Hurst (1949) and illustrated in Fig. 1.6. All stems eventually merge to a completely boundary-dominated, exponential decline condition.

The shapes of the adjacent curves differ only to a small degree. Therefore, achieving a unique match is a difficult task. All stems begin to merge and become indistinguishable at dimensionless time values in the neighborhood of $t_D = 10^{-2}$.

3.2.3 The Arps Curves. The Arps (1945) hyperbolic rate (Eq. 1.9) and time (Eq. 1.19) definitions are expressed in dimensionless form when combined with the dimensionless rate and time (Eqs. 1.31 and 1.32). Recall that these are equations of a line, not solutions to a flow equation.

$$q_{Dd} = \frac{q}{q_i} = \frac{1}{\left(1 + bD_i t\right)^{\frac{1}{b}}}. \quad \dots \dots \dots \dots \dots \quad (3.26)$$

$$t_{Dd} = D_i t = \frac{\left(\frac{q_i}{q}\right)^b - 1}{b}. \quad \dots \dots \dots \dots \dots \quad (3.27)$$

A unit solution was developed by substituting values in the two previous equations to generate curves spanning the range of the Arps exponential, hyperbolic, and harmonic declines. The results of these calculations are shown in **Fig. 3.5.**

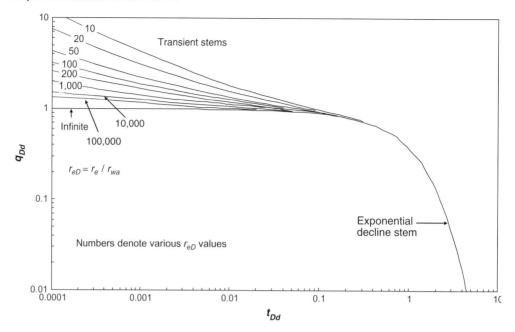

Fig. 3.4—The Fetkovich type curve for transient conditions. All stems merge to the exponential line. Matching should not be attempted when $t_{Dd} > 10^{-2}$ because the stems are essentially the same shape. Adapted from Fetkovich (1980).

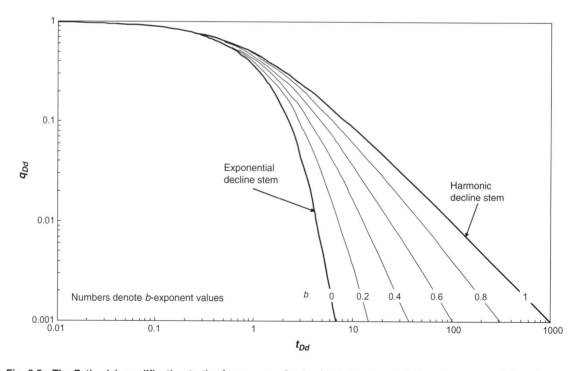

Fig. 3.5—The Fetkovich modification to the Arps curves for $0 \leq b \leq 1$ range. It is difficult to curve match with any degree of certainty for $t_D < 2$ values. Adapted from Fetkovich (1980).

Note: The depletion stems are very similar in the $0.16 < t_{Dd} < 2.0$ range, although the exponential curve is somewhat easier to distinguish than the harmonic curve. The transient and Arps type-curve sets are connected by the solution to the exponential decline curve.

Spivey et al. (1992) superimposed cumulative recovery curves onto the Fetkovich rate-decline curves in an attempt to increase the probability of finding the "most correct" answer. These integrated Fetkovich rate-time curves provide a cumulative production-time relationship.

The Fetkovich type curves were developed to cover the anticipated spectrum of conditions. Generally, short-term production tests are analyzed on the transient side, while long-term production records are analyzed on the Arps side of the type curves. The analysis procedure is straightforward.

3.2.4 Analysis Procedure. *Construct a log-log plot of the field rate-time data on the same scale as the type curve.* Overlay the field production curve on the type curve, and select the most likely match. Short-term production tests should be matched on the transient curves shown in Fig. 3.4, while long-term production declines should be matched with the Fetkovich-Arps curves shown in Fig. 3.5.

Obtain the match points and appropriate stem. The match points are: q, q_{Dd}, t, and t_{Dd}. The dimensionless match points are the easiest to select before the matching process begins.

Select the r_{wa} stem if the transient figure is used. The b stem is determined if the Arps side is applied to the interpretation.

3.2.5 Analysis of Performance—The Transient Side. Extend the field production curve along the fitted type curve to predict future production. Remember: This extrapolation should be performed with care because of the infinite-acting nature of the curves at late time. This extrapolation process can be accomplished with a reasonable degree of certainty only if the production data extends into the Arps side of the type curve.

Permeability-thickness product (formation conductivity), reservoir pore volume, and apparent wellbore radius values may be calculated from the interpretation of match stem and match points. Table 3.1 lists the reservoir information required to complete the calculations.

Reservoir permeability for an oil well may be calculated with Eq. 3.14, while Eqs. 3.15 or 3.16 are employed in this calculation for a gas well.

$$kh = \frac{141.2 B\mu}{p_i - p_{wf}} \left[\ln\left(\frac{r_e}{r_{wa}}\right) - \frac{1}{2} \right] \left[\frac{q}{q_{Dd}} \right]_{m.p.} \qquad \text{(oil well)}$$

or

$$kh = \frac{1,422T}{p_p(p_i) - p_p(p_{wf})} \left[\ln\left(\frac{r_e}{r_{wa}}\right) - \frac{1}{2} \right] \left[\frac{q}{q_{Dd}} \right]_{m.p.} \qquad \text{[gas well, } p_p(p)\text{]}$$

$$kh = \frac{1,422T\mu z}{\left(p_i^2 - p_{wf}^2\right)} \left[\ln\left(\frac{r_e}{r_{wa}}\right) - \frac{1}{2} \right] \left[\frac{q}{q_{Dd}} \right]_{m.p.} \qquad \text{(gas well, } p^2\text{)}$$

Calculate the apparent wellbore radius with Eq. 3.25.

$$r_{wa} = \left[\frac{0.0127k}{\phi\mu c_t \left[(r_{eD})_{m.p.}^2 - 1 \right] \left[\ln(r_{eD})_{m.p.} - \frac{1}{2} \right]} \left[\frac{t}{t_{Dd}} \right]_{m.p.} \right]^{0.5}$$

Use Eq. 3.22 to calculate the drainage area pore volume for an oil well. The units of pore volume in that relationship are reservoir barrels. Eqs. 3.23 and 3.24 express the calculation of the pore volume from a production decline-curve match in a gas reservoir. Eq. 3.23 is given in terms of the real gas pseudopressure and is applicable over the entire pressure range of interest, while the pressure-squared approximation given in Eq. 3.24 is applicable for relatively low-pressure reservoirs (less than 3,000 psia). The pore volume units in the case of a gas reservoir analysis are reservoir cubic feet (rcf).

(Oil well)

$$V_p = \frac{\pi \left(r_e^2 - r_{wa}^2 \right) \phi h}{5.615} = \left[\frac{\bar{B}_o \bar{\mu}_o}{\mu_{oi} \bar{c}_t \left(p_i - p_{wf} \right)} \right] \left[\frac{t}{t_{Dd}} \right]_{m.p.} \left[\frac{q}{q_{Dd}} \right]_{m.p.}$$

or

[Gas well, $p_p(p)$]

$$V_p = \pi \left(r_e^2 - r_{wa}^2 \right) \phi h = \left[\frac{56.557T}{\mu_{gi} \bar{c}_t \left(p_p \left(p_i \right) - p_p \left(p_{wf} \right) \right)} \right] \left[\frac{t}{t_{Dd}} \right]_{m.p.} \left[\frac{q}{q_{Dd}} \right]_{m.p.}$$

(Gas well, p^2)

$$V_p = \pi \left(r_e^2 - r_{wa}^2 \right) \phi h = \left[\frac{56.557T \bar{\mu}_g \bar{z}}{\mu_{gi} \bar{c}_t \left(p_i^2 - p_{wf}^2 \right)} \right] \left[\frac{t}{t_{Dd}} \right]_{m.p.} \left[\frac{q}{q_{Dd}} \right]_{m.p.}$$

3.2.6 Analysis of Performance—The Arps Side. Table 1.1 lists the equations for calculating the future performance characteristics for the Arps equations.

Combine the match points and Eqs. 1.31 and 1.32 to calculate the initial decline and rate coefficients. Extend the production curve line downward along the fitted type curve to predict future production.

The decline rate is constant for the *exponential term*. The initial rate positions the exponential line vertically, while the decline rate characterizes the slope of the line.

The stem match for a *harmonic curve* is $b = 1$. The initial rate and decline rate coefficients must be calculated to apply the rate, time, and cumulative recovery equations.

The stem match for a *hyperbolic curve* varies from $(0 < b < 1)$. The initial rate and decline rate coefficients must be calculated to apply the rate, time, and cumulative recovery equations.

The M-4x well example problem, previously discussed in the Jacob and Lohman infinite-acting section of this chapter, is used to illustrate the calculation procedure for applying the transient portion of the Fetkovich type curve. Theoretically, the Fetkovich type-curve approach should not be applied, because the well test appeared to be infinite-acting. However, the following interpretation results in reasonable answers and demonstrates the interpretation procedure.

Example problems illustrating the Arps definitions discussed for the exponential decline curve in Chapter 4 and the hyperbolic and harmonic decline curves developed in Chapter 5 are also worked in the context of the type-curve approach in their respective sections.

Problem. Apply the Fetkovich type-curve approach to the M-4x well information to estimate permeability and reservoir size. As noted previously, the test was conducted during a 6.7-day period and appears to reflect transient conditions. Therefore, the production history should be analyzed with the transient side of the Fetkovich type curves. Table 3.2 lists the reservoir and test information for the M-4x well (Fetkovich et al. 1987).

Solution. Rate-time data and the type curve were plotted on 1.5-in.-scale, logarithmic graph paper. **Fig. 3.6** shows the overlay of the two rate-time plots. The single square locates the match point. Match points are as follows:

$r_{eD} = 100$, $q_{Dd} = 1.0$, $t_{Dd} = 0.001$, $q = 705$ STB/D, $t = 32$ hours.

The M-4x well was the example problem in the previous Jacob and Lohman infinite-acting reservoir illustration. The solution indicated a good fit between the type and field curve for the infinite-acting case. An equally good solution is a match with the $r_{eD} = 200$, another bounded reservoir decline stem. It is evident that more than one solution is possible.

This example demonstrates that to get a unique decline-curve analysis match using the Fetkovich decline curves, with consistent estimates of all of the system parameters (including well-drainage area and con-

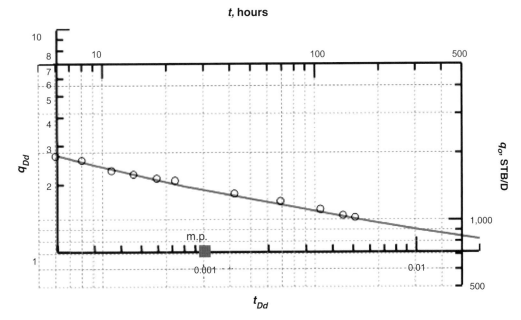

Fig. 3.6—Overlay of the field and type curve match with the r_{eD} = 100 stem M-4x well. The type curve is the solid line, and data are the points.

tacted pore volume), production performance data must be present on both the infinite-acting transient and bounded (late-time) reservoir decline stems. Because the decline data in this example exhibit only an infinite-acting reservoir behavior, the results obtained from a decline analysis in this case do not provide reliable or accurate estimates of the well-drainage area and pore volume, because no boundaries have been observed at the end of the production data. This fundamental principle applies for all inversion problems. *If the behavior of a given parameter is not exhibited in the response function (production performance) being evaluated, then reliable and accurate estimates of that parameter cannot be obtained from the inversion of the data.*

To demonstrate this fact, note the ranges of some of the values of the parameters obtained when evaluating the infinite-acting reservoir production performance data of a well with a Fetkovich finite-reservoir decline-curve analysis. For this example, consider the match on a decline stem with an r_{eD} = 100.

Calculate permeability. The rate match points, r_{eD} value, and requisite reservoir properties are entered into Eq. 3.14.

$$kh = \frac{141.2B\mu}{p_i - p_{wf}} \left[\ln\left(\frac{r_e}{r_{wa}}\right) - \frac{1}{2} \right] \left[\frac{q}{q_{Dd}} \right]_{m.p.}.$$

$$kh = \frac{141.2(1.1)(2.3)}{3,360 - 2,660} \left[\ln(100) - \frac{1}{2} \right] \left[\frac{705}{1} \right] = 1,477 \text{ md-ft}.$$

$$k = \frac{kh}{h} = \frac{1477}{30} = 49.2 \text{ md}.$$

Calculate apparent wellbore radius. Real and dimensionless time match points, the match r_{eD} stem, and requisite reservoir properties are entered into Eq. 3.25 to calculate the apparent wellbore radius. Time units in the equation are days, while the test data were recorded in hours; therefore, include a 24-hour/day time conversion term in the calculation to cancel the time units.

$$r_{wa} = \left[\frac{0.0127k}{\phi \mu c_t \left[\left(r_{eD}\right)_{m.p.}^2 - 1 \right] \left[\ln\left(r_{eD}\right)_{m.p.} - \frac{1}{2} \right] \left[\frac{t}{t_{Dd}} \right]_{m.p.}} \right]^{0.5}.$$

$$r_{wa} = \left[\frac{0.0127(49.2)}{0.25(2.3)(3 \times 10^{-6})\left[100^2 - 1 \right] \left[\ln(100) - \frac{1}{2} \right] \left[\frac{32}{24(0.001)} \right]} \right]^{0.5} = 108.5 \text{ ft.}$$

Calculate skin factor. Calculate the skin around the wellbore with Eq. 3.7.

$$S = -\ln\left(\frac{r_{wa}}{r_w} \right) = -\ln\left(\frac{108.5}{0.328} \right) = -5.8.$$

Calculate well-drainage volume. Calculate the well-drainage volume with Eq. 3.23.

$$V_p = \frac{\pi \left(r_e^2 - r_{wa}^2 \right) \phi h}{5.615} = \left[\frac{\bar{B}_o \bar{\mu}_o}{\mu_{oi} \bar{c}_t \left(p_i - p_{wf} \right)} \right] \left[\frac{t}{t_{Dd}} \right]_{m.p.} \left[\frac{q}{q_{Dd}} \right]_{m.p.}.$$

$$V_p = \left[\frac{(1.1)(2.3)}{(2.3)(3 \times 10^{-6})(3,360 - 2,660)} \right] \left[\frac{32}{24(0.001)} \right] \left[\frac{705}{1} \right] = 49.238 \times 10^7 \text{ res bbl.}$$

$$V_B = \frac{49.238 \times 10^7 \text{ res bbl}}{(0.25)(7,758 \text{ res bbl/acre-ft})} = 253,870 \text{ acre-ft.}$$

Note: The reservoir bulk volume previously given reflects the correct pore volume and the fact that you are calculating bulk volume, not pore volume. Also, one must divide by the effective porosity (ϕ) to obtain that answer. The well-drainage area is therefore also evaluated using the reservoir bulk volume (normalized by the net pay) to obtain the well drainage area.

Well drainage area:

$$A = \frac{V_B}{h} = \frac{253,870 \text{ acre-ft}}{30 \text{ ft}} = 8,462 \text{ acres}$$

An equally good match may also be obtained with the $r_{eD} = 200$ curve. **Table 3.3** compares the results of the calculations for the infinite acting—Jacob and Lohman solution, $r_{eD} = 100$, and $r_{eD} = 200$ curve matches. Note: The permeability and apparent skin effect values calculated from the data developed from the three different matches are generally comparable. However, as should be expected, reservoir volume and drainage area values are all much greater than can possibly be actually drained by the well. Differences in the reservoir

TABLE 3.3—COMPARISON OF TYPE-CURVE ANALYSIS: M-4x WELL			
Match	$r_{eD} = \infty$	$r_{eD} = 100$	$r_{eD} = 200$
k	45.9	49.2	57.5
r_{wa}, ft	83.8	108.5	54.2
S	−5.5	−5.8	−5.1
V_p, acre-ft	Infinite	253,870	253,870
A, acre	Infinite	8,462	8,462

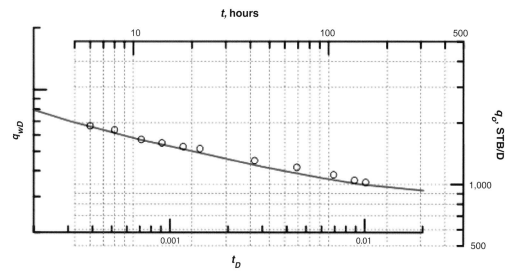

Fig. 3.7—Matching the field data to a portion of the infinite-acting Fetkovich and Thrasher type curve proves that the drainage volume calculation cannot be applied to the M-4x well test. The symbols are the field data points, while the solid line represents the type curve.

outer-boundary estimate r_{eD} value selected do not permit better definition of the drainage area. Note: The pore volume derived from the decline analysis match points (the right sides of Eq. 3.22 in this case for an oil reservoir analysis, or Eqs. 3.23 or 3.24 for a gas reservoir analysis) is independent of the matched decline stem r_{eD} value selected. Comparison of the values listed in the table indicate the formation effective permeability and apparent steady-state skin effect may be determined with a relative degree of reliability for engineering purposes, even though only the infinite-acting reservoir performance has been exhibited in the data. Alternatively, the exercise illustrates that reliable estimation of the reservoir pore volume and well-drainage area is not possible if only infinite-acting reservoir well-performance data are available.

The previous discussion shows that applying the transient side of the Fetkovich type curves to match field data and calculate an apparent drainage volume for the M-4x well can result in a fairly wide disparity of answers. The problem arose because the basic tenet requiring an indication of the production curve extending into the Arps side of the type curve was not followed. **Fig. 3.7** presents a match of a portion of the Fetkovich and Thrasher type curve (Fig. 3.3) with the M-4x well data.

The match was obtained in the early-time, infinite-acting portion of the type curve even before the digression of the $r_e/r_w = 10$ stem. Application of the Fetkovich and Thrasher (1979) type curve verifies that the well test remained in the infinite-acting portion, and a drainage volume cannot be calculated from the well test information.

Chapter 4

The Exponential Decline Curve

Arps (1945) defined an exponential decline as existing when the loss in production rate per unit time is proportional to the production rate. The same definition also applies to either the Johnson and Bollens (1927) definition of the loss ratio or the Vance (1961) definition of a constant percentage decline. Any of the three definitions result in the same straightline, semilog rate-time curve presentation. The exponential production decline curve is also called a geometric or semilog decline.

Fig. 1.2 indicated that a rectangular scale, production rate-time plot generally forms a concave, upward-trending curve. However, Fig. 1.4 showed that the exponential decline curve forms a straight line on a semilog rate-time plot. Fitting an exponential curve to approximate well-performance history is a widely used forecasting tool because of the ease of extrapolating a straight line forward in time. The semilog rate-time plot of the performance history for the example Drew-Buzz Well 1, shown in **Fig. 4.1,** reflects an exponential decline curve.

Two different sets of equations may be chosen to model the exponential decline curve. Equations representing the following:

1. An incremental or constant percentage decline reflecting similar decline rates measured during successive and equal time increments.
2. The continuous decline case defined by the exponential line equation shown as Eq. 1.8.

Either equation set represents a different way to forecast performance from the same exponential curve. The results of the calculations, using either method, produce the same forecast as long as the proper definitions and equations are applied.

Arps (1945) and, more particularly, Brons (1963) recognized that an exponential decline curve reflects depletion of a closed reservoir exhibiting essentially a constant compressibility system. Moderate-to-low GOR oil and high-pressure gas reservoirs are instances of essentially constant compressibility systems. Unfortunately, these facts have generally been lost in the mist of time. Later work by Fetkovich (1980) and Cox (1978) related the exponential decline to the solution of the diffusivity equation for a closed reservoir producing at a constant BHFP. This theoretical development verified the earlier observations of Arps (1945) and Brons (1963).

The first part of the following discussion develops the equations related to either the constant percentage or continuous decline definitions. Eq. 1.1 represented the incremental production loss during a finite period of time. For a unit increment in time ($\Delta t = 1$), this expression can be reduced to the following simplified form:

$$d = \frac{q_1 - q_2}{q_1}.$$

A rewritten form of this relationship is as follows:

$$\frac{q_2}{q_1} = 1 - d. \quad \dots\dots\dots\dots\dots\dots\dots\dots\dots\dots\dots\dots\dots\dots\dots\dots\dots\dots\dots\dots\dots \quad (4.1)$$

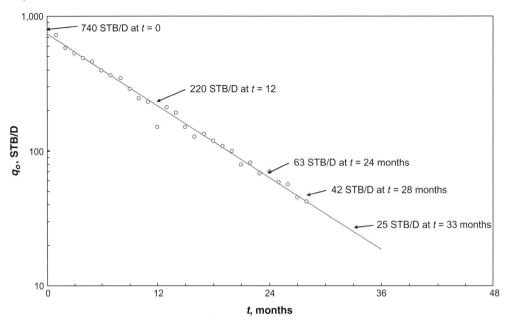

Fig. 4.1—The semilog rate-time plot, Drew-Buzz Well 1. Extending the line beyond the last data point at Month 28 to estimate future production is a straightforward process.

The Arps (1945) equation (Eq. 1.8) for an exponential decline curve states that q_i is the rate at initial time when $t = 0$, and D is the continuous decline rate. The interval t spans the time for the producing rate to decline from an initial condition at q_i to a later condition at q_2.

$$\frac{q_2}{q_i} = \exp(-Dt).$$

Expanding Eq. 1.8 into the following form with the assumptions of equal time increments of $t = 1$ and $q_1 = q_i$:

$$\frac{q_2}{q_1} = \frac{q_3}{q_2} = \dots = \frac{q_n}{q_{n-1}} = \exp(-D). \quad \dots\dots\dots\dots\dots\dots\dots\dots\dots\dots\dots\dots\dots \quad (4.2)$$

Combining Eq. 4.1 and Eq. 4.2 establishes the following identity:

$$d = 1 - \exp(-D). \quad \dots\dots\dots\dots\dots\dots\dots\dots\dots\dots\dots\dots\dots\dots\dots\dots \quad (4.3)$$

Conversely, Eq. 4.3 can be rewritten in terms of solving for D.

$$D = -\ln(1 - d). \quad \dots\dots\dots\dots\dots\dots\dots\dots\dots\dots\dots\dots\dots\dots\dots\dots \quad (4.4)$$

As expected, combining Eqs. 4.2 and 4.3 results in the definition for the constant percentage decline rate shown as Eq. 1.1. Vance (1961) applied essentially the same technique to calculate successive decline rate values measured during equal time intervals. Defining the starting point on a straight line does not require a specific target, such as initial time, because the slope remains constant. One is not very "lucky" when studying the curved hyperbolic and harmonic cases.

Eq. 1.1 satisfies the Arps (1945) general definition of a decline curve and forms the basis for determining the constant percentage decline rate, d. The continuous exponential decline rate, D, is developed from a direct application of Eq. 1.8, when q_1 is assumed to represent the starting point of the curve, and q_2 is a later rate.

Convention assumes the decline rate is expressed in terms of %/yr, not as a yearly fraction.

4.1 The Constant Percentage Decline

The constant percentage analysis method assumes that the incremental difference of the producing rate measured between two production periods defines the decline rate.

4.1.1 Development of Equations. Solve the logarithmic form of Eq. 1.8 as a function of time. The initial rate, q_i, can be changed to the q_1 form to represent any starting point time selected on the straight line of the logarithmic rate-time plot.

$$\ln \frac{q_2}{q_1} = -Dt. \quad\dots\dots\dots\dots\dots\dots\dots\dots\dots\dots\dots\dots\dots\dots \quad (4.5)$$

Solving Eq. 4.5 for time and combining with Eq. 4.4 results in an expression defining the time interval in terms of the constant percentage decline rate and any two successive rates:

$$t = \frac{\ln\left(\dfrac{q_2}{q_1}\right)}{\ln\left(1 - d\right)}. \quad\dots\dots\dots\dots\dots\dots\dots\dots\dots\dots\dots\dots \quad (4.6)$$

Manipulate Eq. 4.6 to develop a rate equation expressed in terms of the constant percentage decline rate.

$$q_2 = q_1 \left(1 - d\right)^t. \quad\dots\dots\dots\dots\dots\dots\dots\dots\dots\dots\dots\dots\dots \quad (4.7)$$

Develop the cumulative production equation by integrating the rate equation over the range. Cumulative oil production, N_p, or the cumulative gas production, G_p, may be substituted into the more all-inclusive Q_p term for any particular case study.

$$Q_p = \frac{q_2 - q_1}{\ln\left(1 - d\right)}. \quad\dots\dots\dots\dots\dots\dots\dots\dots\dots\dots\dots\dots\dots \quad (4.8)$$

The time scale of the calculated decline rate cannot be directly interpolated because the basis of the decline rate must be recalculated when changing time units. The following two expressions convert yearly decline rates to monthly or daily rates. Similar relationships can be easily developed for other time interval combinations.

To convert from rate/year to rate/month:

$$d_y = 1 - \left(1 - d_m\right)^{12}. \quad\dots\dots\dots\dots\dots\dots\dots\dots\dots\dots\dots\dots \quad (4.9)$$

To convert from rate/year to rate/day:

$$d_y = 1 - \left(1 - d_d\right)^{365}. \quad\dots\dots\dots\dots\dots\dots\dots\dots\dots\dots \quad (4.10)$$

The pertinent equations for forecasting constant percentage and continuous exponential decline performance are listed in **Table 4.1.** Note: The meaning of q_i and q_1 are interchangeable, signifying the beginning of the time period.

4.1.2 Analysis Procedure. Construct a logarithmic rate-vs.-time plot similar to the one shown in Fig. 4.1 to verify that a reasonably straight line can be drawn through the data points. Emphasis should be placed on matching more recent data at the expense of possibly excluding some of the very-early-time measurements, because future performance should more closely follow the trend of the late-time information. The absence of a reasonable straightline fit to the data indicates that the decline curve is not exponential in nature.

Remember, there should be a certain amount of judgment implied in any curve fit. The procedure is not only a statistical exercise, but should be realistic and believable.

Calculate the constant percentage decline rate. Pick any two points on the straight line, preferably 12 months apart, and read the production rate equivalent to these times. This value represents the decline rate

TABLE 4.1—CONSTANT PERCENTAGE AND CONTINUOUS EXPONENTIAL EQUATIONS

	Constant Percentage	Continuous Exponential
Decline rate	$d = \dfrac{q_1 - q_2}{q_1}$	$D = \dfrac{\ln\left(\dfrac{q_1}{q_2}\right)}{t}$
Producing rate	$q_2 = q_1(1-d)^t$	$q_2 = q_1 \exp(-Dt)$
Elapsed time	$t = \dfrac{\ln\left(\dfrac{q_2}{q_1}\right)}{\ln(1-d)}$	$t = \dfrac{\ln\left(\dfrac{q_1}{q_2}\right)}{D}$
Cumulative production	$Q_p = \dfrac{q_2 - q_1}{\ln(1-d)}$	$Q_p = \dfrac{q_1 - q_2}{D}$

spanning the period as q_1 declines to q_2. Apply Eq. 1.1 to calculate the constant percentage decline rate. Apply Eqs. 4.9 or 4.10 to convert the time scale of the decline rate if so desired.

Calculate future performance. Extrapolate along the straightline fit of the historical rate-time data to the time frame of interest, or use Eq. 4.7 to determine future production rates. The reference rate q_1 can be any point on the line. The time difference between the reference and the flow rate of interest is t.

Time interval between any two production rates. Apply Eq. 4.6.

Cumulative production between any two production rates. Apply Eq. 4.8.

Problem. The Drew-Buzz Well 1 example problem illustrates the concepts developed in this section. Fig. 4.1 shows the semilog rate-time plot of the production history. Recorded production declines from 720 STB/D at initial conditions to 42 STB/D at 28 months.

Solution. A good straightline fit of the production data is achieved when a straight line is drawn through the plotted data. Backward extrapolation of the straight line to initial time indicates $q_i = 740$ STB/D at initial time when $t = 0$. Thereafter, all rate-time estimates are interpolated from the straightline approximation.

Find the constant percentage decline rate for the performance curve. Calculate the constant percentage decline rate from the straight line drawn through the data points. Rate values of 220 STB/D at 12 months and 63 STB/D at 24 months are interpolated from Fig. 4.1. Remember: The line approximation of the production data forms the basis for all performance predictions once the smoothed line has been drawn through the data points. Enter rate-time values measured at any time period into Eq. 1.1 to calculate the decline rate as long as one is aware of the time span between the two endpoints.

$$d = \frac{q_1 - q_2}{q_1} = \frac{(220 - 63)100}{220} = 71.4\%/\text{yr}.$$

Convert the decline rate-time units from %/yr to %/month. Refer to Eq. 4.9 for the month-year conversion equation. Rearrange Eq. 4.9 to obtain the following conversion relationship between yearly and monthly decline rates.

$$d_m = 1 - (1 - d_y)^{\frac{1}{12}} = 1 - (1 - 0.714)^{\frac{1}{12}} = 9.9\%/\text{month}$$

Table 4.2 presents a comparison of the decline rate related to different time units. Note: The difference between declined rates for the different time units is not linear.

Calculate the expected producing rate at 33 months. Extrapolate the straightline fit of the data forward to Month 33 to select the rate from the semilog plot, or apply Eq. 4.7 to calculate the future rate.

The straightline approximation at 28 months indicates $q = 42$ STB/D, which happens to be the equivalent of the measured rate of $q = 42$ STB/D. Extrapolation of the straight line to Month 33 indicates $q = 25$ STB/D.

**TABLE 4.2—COMPARISON OF DECLINE RATES
CALCULATED ACCORDING TO DIFFERENT TIME UNITS**

Monthly decline rate, %/month	9.9
Semiannual decline rate, %/6 months	46.5
Annual decline rate, %/yr	71.4

The following example shows constant percentage decline rates expressed in month or year units calculated at the same producing rate as long as the time units cancel. Apply Eq. 4.7 to solve for the future producing rate. Assume that initial time or $t = 0$ occurs 28 months before the last recorded field measurement for this case.

$$q_2 = q_1 (1 - d)^t = 42(1 - 0.714)^{\frac{(33-28) \text{ month}}{12 \text{ months/yr}}} = 25 \text{ STB/D}.$$

Apply the 9.9%/month decline rate to solve for the future producing rate:

$$q_2 = q_1 (1 - d)^t = 42(1 - 0.099)^{(33-28)} = 25 \text{ STB/D}.$$

The answers remain the same as long as the proper units are included in the equations.

Oil reserves. How much oil is produced as the well declines from the current time at Month 28 (when $q = 42$ STB/D) to the 10-STB/D EL? How long is this time interval?

Calculate cumulative oil production with Eq. 4.8. Remember: The units must cancel to yield a volume expression. The rate units are STB/D, while the decline rate units are %/yr. The units do not cancel, unless the conversion term of 365 days/year is included in the equation.

$$N_p = \frac{q_2 - q_1}{\ln(1 - d)} = \frac{(10 - 42)(365)}{\ln(1 - 0.714)} = 9{,}331 \text{ STB}.$$

$$t = \frac{\ln\left(\dfrac{q_2}{q_1}\right)}{\ln(1 - d)} = \frac{\ln\left(\dfrac{10}{42}\right)}{\ln(1 - 0.714)} = 1.15 \text{ years, or} \approx 13.8 \text{ months}.$$

The time frame may be easily calculated by extending the straight line down to the intersection of the 10-STB/D limit. The time difference between the two rates is approximately 14 months.

4.2 The Continuous Exponential Decline

The Arps (1945) differential equations defining the fundamental decline-curve relationships provide the starting point for developing the continuous exponential decline concept. The exponential line presented as Eq. 1.8 forms the basis for the rate, time, and cumulative production equations developed in Chapter 1 and listed in Table 1.1. The continuous decline equations are compared to the constant percentage equations in Table 4.1. Note: The continuous exponential decline calculations are more compact and easier to apply than the equations representing the constant percentage decline calculation procedure.

4.2.1 Analysis Procedure. The analysis procedure is the same as the one followed in the Section 4.1.2. The only difference is in the equations included in the calculations. Theoretically, the initial decline rate and producing rate should be used in the following equations. However, the constant decline rate implies that $D_i = D$ occurs for all cases, and the initial rate q_i can be chosen at any point q_1 on the straight line. The equations presented in Table 4.1 have been modified to account for this fact.

Calculate the decline rate, D. Select any two rate-time values on the straightline approximation of the performance history. Preferably, these two rate points are selected 12 months apart to facilitate calculating the decline rate in %/yr units. Apply Eq. 1.12 to calculate the decline rate.

Calculate future performance. Either extrapolate along the straightline fit of the historical rate-time data to the time period of interest, or apply Eq. 1.8. The reference rate is any starting point selected on the line.

Calculate the time interval between any two production rates. Apply Eq. 1.13.

Calculate the cumulative production between any two production rates. Apply Eq. 1.16. The rate and decline rate-time units must cancel to result in a volume measurement. Rate units are often expressed in volume/day, while decline rate units are %/yr. For this case, include a 365-days/year multiplier in the calculation to cancel the time units.

Problem. The principles of the continuous exponential decline method are applied to the Drew-Buzz Well 1 performance data. The semilog rate-time plot is shown as Fig. 4.1. Determine the following characteristics; D, q_2, and N_p.

Solution. Apply Eq. 1.12 to the straightline interpretation of the semilog rate-vs.-time performance plot shown in Fig. 4.1 to calculate the decline rate. Rates of 220 STB/D at 12 months and 63 STB/D at 24 months were read from the straight line. In this instance, initial time was chosen to be at 12 months.

$$D = \frac{\ln\left(\dfrac{q_1}{q_2}\right)}{t} = \frac{\ln\left(\dfrac{220}{63}\right)}{(1 \text{ year})}(100) = 125 \text{ \% / yr}$$

Compare the constant percentage decline rate, $d = 71.4\%/\text{yr}$, to the continuous decline rate, $D = 125\%/\text{yr}$, calculated from the same example problem. The difference in these values is an example of the need to apply the proper equations when calculating future characteristics. The relationship between the two definitions for an exponential decline curve is discussed in the following section (4.2.2).

Convert the %/yr decline rate D to %/month. Convert the decline rate value from %/yr to %/month. Dividing the yearly decline rate number by 12 changes the decline rate to %/month.

$$(125\%/\text{yr})\left(\frac{1}{12 \text{ months/yr}}\right) = 10.4\%/\text{month}$$

Calculate the producing rate expected to occur at 33 months. Extrapolate the straight line outward, or apply Eq. 1.8 to calculate the producing rate at the end of 33 months. Recall that the last recorded data point extrapolated to the straightline approximation was 42 STB/D at 28 months. Ensure that time and decline rate values are expressed in the same time units.

$$q_2 = q_1 \exp(-Dt) = 42\exp\left[-1.25\left(\frac{5 \text{ months}}{12 \text{ months/yr}}\right)\right] = 25 \text{ STB/D}.$$

$$q_2 = q_1 \exp(-Dt) = 42\exp\left[-0.104(5 \text{ months})\right] = 25 \text{ STB/D}.$$

Calculate cumulative oil production for the period spanning the decline from 42 STB/D to the EL. Apply Eq. 1.16 to calculate the remaining production.

$$N_p = \frac{q_1 - q_2}{D} = \frac{(42 - 10)(365 \text{ days/yr})}{(1.25/\text{yr})} = 9,344 \text{ STB}.$$

Compare the answers obtained by the constant percentage and continuous decline equations for the same example problem. The answers are essentially the same, even though the calculated decline rates are different.

4.2.2 The Type-Curve Approach. *Problem.* Apply the Fetkovich type-curve analysis method to determine the characteristics of the Drew-Buzz Well 1 example problem. Determine the following characteristics:

- Decline rate
- Initial producing rate

- Producing rate at 33 months
- Remaining oil to be produced when the EL is 10 STB/D

Solution. Overlay the Fetkovich type curve on the field curve when both are plotted on the same scale, obtain a match, and develop a set of match points. The overlay of the two curves is shown in **Fig. 4.2.**

Match points: $q_{Dd} = 0.1$, $t_{Dd} = 1$, $q = 76$ STB/D, $t = 10$ months

Calculate the decline rate and initial producing rate. Apply rewritten versions of Eqs. 1.31 and 1.32 to calculate the initial producing rate and decline rate from the match point information.

$$q_i = \frac{q}{q_{Dd}} = \frac{76}{0.1} = 760 \text{ STB/D}.$$

$$D_i = \frac{t_{Dd}}{t} = \frac{1}{10} = 0.1/\text{month, or } 120\%/\text{yr}$$

Calculate the producing rate at 28 and 33 months. Extend the field curve along the type curve to predict production.

Extrapolation of the curve indicates $q = 42$ STB/D at $t = 28$ month.

Extrapolation of the curve indicates $q = 24$ STB/D at $t = 33$ months.

Calculate the remaining oil to be produced. Apply Eq. 1.16 to calculate the volume of oil expected to be produced from the last historical data point at $t = 28$ months, when $q = 42$ STB/D, to the EL of 10 STB/D.

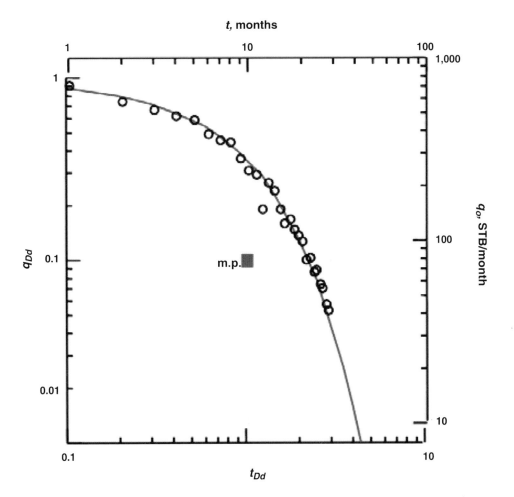

Fig. 4.2—Field- and type-curve match, the Drew-Buzz Well 1 exponential decline example.

$$N_p = \frac{q_1 - q_2}{D} = \frac{(42-10)(365 \text{ days/yr})}{(1.2/\text{yr})} = 9{,}733 \text{ STB}.$$

This answer is essentially the same as those obtained by the conventional methods discussed in the two previous sections.

4.3 Comparing Exponential Declines

The continuous and constant percentage exponential decline rate values are different even though each is based on Eq. 1.8. The following discussion relates and compares the two methods.

4.3.1 Development of Equations. Eq. 4.3 defines the relationship between the two exponential decline rate definitions in terms of solving for the constant percentage decline rate, while Eq. 4.4 provides the relationship when the continuous decline rate is treated as the unknown value.

The solid line in **Fig. 4.3** compares the relative decline rate values for the constant percentage and continuous decline definitions. The 45° slope existing up to a 20% decline reflects a similarity between the two different methods. However, the continuous decline rate increases quite dramatically when compared to the constant percentage decline rate values after this point.

Problem. The effective decline rate was calculated to be 71.4% in the previous example problem. Apply Eq. 4.4 to calculate the continuous decline rate. Compare this answer with the continuous decline rate value calculated in the previous section.

Solution.

$$D = -\ln(1-d) = -\ln(1-0.714) = 1.252, \text{ or } 125.2\%$$

The value is very close to the previous answer of $D = 125\%$ calculated with Eq. 1.1.

4.4 Rate-Cumulative Recovery Curve

The rate-cumulative recovery curve is not widely applied. In reality, this plot is a very powerful tool, because changes in the decline rate are translated directly into changing reserves estimates. Producing rate values developed from the semilog rate-time plot must be converted to cumulative totals to estimate reserves.

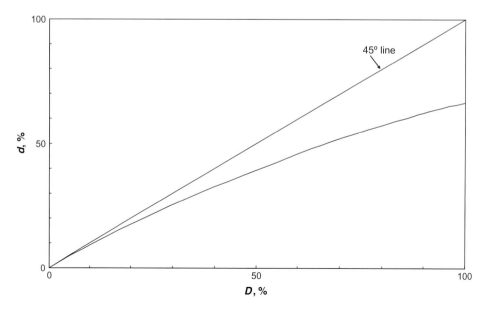

Fig. 4.3—Comparison between the constant percentage and instantaneous decline rates. The two definitions for exponential decline rate begin to diverge significantly in the $D > 20\%$ region.

4.4.1 Development of Equations. Eq. 1.17 is in the form of an equation of a straight line. This relationship is presented in this discussion for convenience.

$$q_2 = -Q_p D + q_i$$

Eq. 1.17 reflects the straightline relationship for an exponential decline production curve when rate-cumulative production data are plotted on a rectangular scale. The slope of the line represents the decline rate. Refer to Fig. 1.3 to compare the difference between the rate-cumulative recovery plots for the exponential, hyperbolic, and harmonic curves.

Problem: Drew-Buzz Well 1. Production and cumulative production data for Drew-Buzz Well 1 plotted on a coordinate scale. The resulting plot is shown as **Fig. 4.4.** Two straight lines are apparent. Evidently, operating conditions changed at approximately the 160,000-STB mark. These changes caused a decrease in expected ultimate recovery when the lines are extrapolated to the 10-STB/D EL.

The slope of the straight line represents the continuous exponential decline rate. Note: This decline rate is very close to the 125%/yr decline rate calculated with Eq. 1.12.

$$D = \frac{-(y_2 - y_1)}{x_2 - x_1} = \frac{-(200 - 400 \text{ STB/D})(365 \text{ days/yr})(100)}{(156,000 - 97,000 \text{ STB})} = 123.7\%/\text{yr}$$

The ability of the figure to readily define ultimate recovery as well as reflect changing operating conditions on recovery is apparent. Remember: Operating or reservoir depletion characteristics are assumed to remain constant over the range of interpretation; therefore, significant changes in operating conditions should affect the shape of the exponential curve.

4.4.2 Effect of Offsetting Well Example. Marsh (1928) applied the rate-cumulative recovery plot to determine the effects of changing reservoir drainage size or operating conditions on ultimate recovery. **Fig. 4.5** illustrates the effect of choking back an HGOR well on the producing characteristics of an offsetting well. The rate-time and rate-cumulative production plots show that the decline rate changed from 249%/yr to approximately 96%/yr when the HGOR well was shut in. Expected ultimate recovery was also affected. The rate-cumulative production plot is a highly visual presentation showing that ultimate recovery was increased from 119,000 to 160,000 STB when the drainage area increased because of shutting in the offset well.

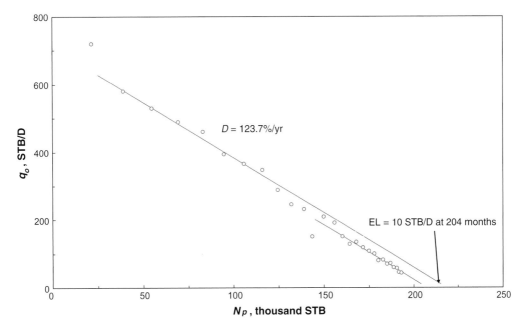

Fig. 4.4—The rate-cumulative production plot, Drew-Buzz Well 1. A change in the operating conditions probably caused the shifting of decline-curve shift at the 155,000-STB cumulative production level.

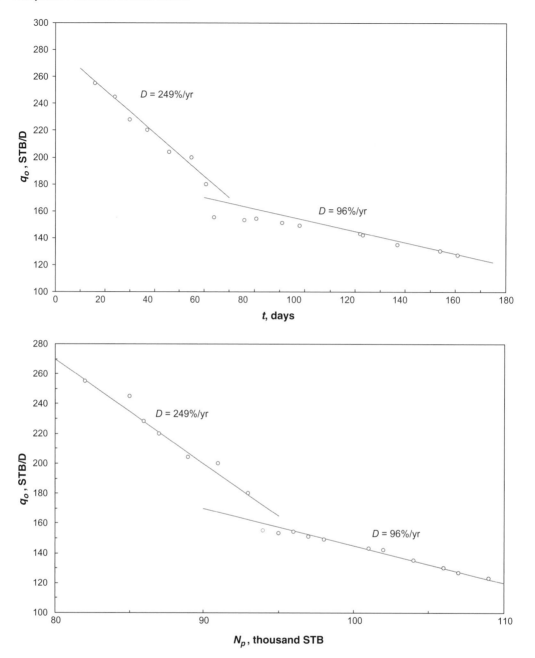

Fig. 4.5—The effect of choking back an HGOR well on the producing characteristics of an offsetting well. Adapted from Marsh (1928).

4.4.3 Effect of the HGOR Example. The effect of changing the choke size on the producing rate and GOR for a well was discussed by Allen (1931) and is shown in **Fig. 4.6.** Reducing the choke size increased the BHFP, which in turn, reduced the gas volume flowing to the wellbore.

Straight lines representing each producing segment can be drawn through the production data. Recall that the slope of the line of the rate-cumulative production plot represents the decline rate. Each significant change in the producing GOR causes a change in the slope of the oil decline rate for each segment. The production history is divided into four segments, and the production rate levels seem to be controlled by the producing GOR. A rapidly declining rate and an increasing GOR are apparent during the first producing segment. The

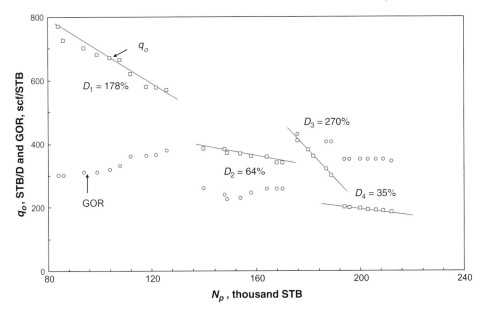

Fig. 4.6—The effect of changing GOR on ultimate recovery. GOR is seen to be a direct function of the producing rate. Adapted from Allen (1931).

decline rate was calculated to be 178% at early time when the GOR was climbing in a stepwise manner. Good straightline relationships were established during the remaining three producing segments.

The intersection of each line on the x-axis represents the expected ultimate recovery if the production practice characterized by that segment is maintained throughout the life of the well. Reserves are a function of production practice.

4.5 Solution to the Diffusivity Equation

The following discussion relates the exponential decline curve of the constant pressure solution to the diffusivity equation for a closed reservoir with a slightly compressible system. This relationship permits calculating reservoir volume and permeability when an exponential performance decline curve exists.

4.5.1 Development of Equations. The constant pressure solution for production from a closed, circular reservoir of constant compressibility was shown as Eq. 1.44. Time spans the interval, because the well was placed on production. Total time includes transient, transition, and boundary-dominated flow periods.

$$\ln q = \ln \left\{ \frac{kh\left(p_i - p_{wf}\right)}{141.2B\mu\left[\ln\left(\dfrac{r_e}{r_w}\right) - \dfrac{3}{4} + s\right]} \right\} - \left\{ \left(\frac{0.00633kt}{\phi\mu c_t r_w^2}\right) \frac{2}{\left(\dfrac{r_e}{r_w}\right)^2 \left[\ln\left(\dfrac{r_e}{r_w}\right) - \dfrac{3}{4} + s\right]} \right\}$$

Plotting terms for the components of the equation of the straight line represented by Eq. 1.44 are as follows:
  y plotting variable: producing rate, $\ln q$ (STB/D).
  x plotting variable: time, t (days).

Fig. 1.9 presents an idealized example of such a plot. Two outcome coefficients represent the slope and intercept values for the straight line, given by Eqs. 4.11 and 4.12, respectively.

$$\text{Slope, } D = \frac{0.0127k}{\phi\mu c_t r_e^2 \left[\ln\left(\dfrac{r_e}{r_w}\right) - \dfrac{3}{4} + S\right]}, \text{ fraction/yr.} \quad \dots\dots\dots\dots\dots\dots\dots\dots\dots (4.11)$$

The equation (Eq. 1.44) indicates that the slope of the semilog rate-time plot is equivalent to the decline rate, D.

$$\text{Intercept} = \frac{kh\left(p_i - p_{wf}\right)}{141.2B\mu\left[\ln\left(\dfrac{r_e}{r_w}\right) - \dfrac{3}{4} + S\right]}, \quad \text{STB/D}. \dotfill (4.12)$$

The initial rate q_i is a theoretical value that may not coincide with the field-measured initial rate. Rewrite Eq. 1.11 in a shortened form by including Eqs. 4.11 and 4.12 into the expression.

$$\ln q = -Dt + \ln q_i \dotfill (4.13)$$

The exponential decline properties in Eq. 4.13 are apparent when compared to Eq. 1.11. Eq. 4.14, defining the pore volume of the reservoir in units of rcf, is obtained when the expression $\ln\left(\dfrac{r_e}{r_w}\right) - \dfrac{3}{4} + S$ is used to equate the slope definition shown in Eq. 4.11 with the intercept definition of Eq. 4.12.

$$V_p = \phi hA = \frac{5.615q_iB}{Dc_t\left(p_i - p_{wf}\right)}. \dotfill (4.14)$$

The previous equation shows that the reservoir pore volume or drainage area can be calculated when a continuous decline rate is interpreted from the semilog rate-time plot. Extrapolate the straight line of the semilog rate-time plot back to initial time when $t = 0$ to determine the initial producing rate. Rewrite Eq. 4.12 to evaluate the reservoir permeability in millidarcies.

$$k = \frac{141.2qB\mu\left[\ln\left(\dfrac{r_e}{r_w}\right) - \dfrac{3}{4} + S\right]}{h\left(p_i - p_{wf}\right)}. \dotfill (4.15)$$

The discussion shows that both the OOIP and the reservoir permeability can be calculated if the production decline curve exhibits exponential decline characteristics. Note: These equations furnish the same reservoir parameters that may be determined from a transient pressure drawdown test. However, one should remember that formation damage effects can mask true formation permeability.

4.5.2 Analysis Procedure. Plot the reservoir performance data on a semilog rate-time scale, and determine the presence of a straightline approximation as the first order of business. The absence of a straightline approximation of the production data negates the validity of this analysis procedure.

Determine the properties of the exponential decline curve. Apply Eq. 1.12 to calculate the continuous decline rate, and extrapolate the straight line back to initial time to determine the initial production rate. Ensure that these values are expressed in the proper units.

$$D = \frac{\ln\left(\dfrac{q_i}{q_2}\right)}{t}, \quad \text{fraction/year}$$

Develop the reservoir parameters from the field and well files. The input parameters required to apply Eqs. 4.14 and 4.15 are listed in Table 3.1 in the discussion of the Jacob and Lohman type curve.

Calculate system compressibility with Eq. 3.8.

$$c_t = S_oc_o + S_wc_w + S_gc_g + c_f$$

Apply Eq. 4.14 to calculate drainage volume.

$$V_p = \phi h A = \frac{5.615 q_i B}{D c_t \left(p_i - p_{wf} \right)}$$

Dividing the calculated value of the pore volume by the reservoir average thickness and porosity results in an estimate of drainage area. Apply Eq. 4.15 to calculate reservoir permeability.

$$k = \frac{141.2 q B \mu \left[\ln\left(\frac{r_e}{r_w} \right) - \frac{3}{4} + S \right]}{h \left(p_i - p_{wf} \right)}$$

Calculate the time to attain pseudosteady-state or boundary-dominated conditions, given in units of days. Use the time approximation shown as Eq. 1.45.

$$t_{pss} \approx \frac{40 \phi \mu c_t r_e^2}{k}$$

Problem. An example problem by Cox (1978) of the Tiger Ridge well illustrates these concepts. The production history is shown in **Fig. 4.7,** while the reservoir rock and fluid characteristics are shown in **Table 4.3**.

Reservoir permeability was calculated to be 0.3 md from transient pressure test information, and the wellbore skin is zero. The BHFP is assumed to be zero because the well was "pumped off" during most of its life. Unfortunately, this is not a particularly good assumption. Actual reservoir pore volume and permeability values should be greater than the calculated values, because the $p_{wf} = 0$ assumption is probably not accurate.

Solution. Extrapolation of a straight line drawn through the production decline curve back to initial time determines the decline and initial producing rates. Note: The initial producing rate is not the first measured rate. It is the rate measured on the straight line. How many production segments are evident? Two—there is an initial, rather steep decline (probably transient in nature) and then a more moderate slope extension. Apply Eq. 1.12 to calculate the continuous decline rate.

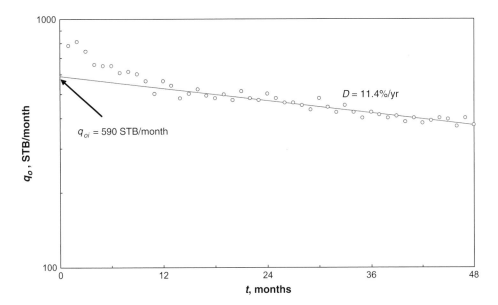

Fig. 4.7—The Tiger Ridge production decline curve. Note: The theoretical and field initial rates are not the same. Adapted from Cox (1978).

TABLE 4.3—TIGER RIDGE RESERVOIR AND CHARACTERISTICS			
A = 40 acres	r_e = 745 ft	ϕ = 15%	h = 42 ft
c_t = 15x10^{-6} psi^{-1}	k = 0.3 md	μ_o = 1 cp	
B_o = 1.25 RB/STB	r_w = 0.33 ft	p_i = 2,100 psi	

$$D = \frac{\ln\left(\dfrac{q_i}{q_2}\right)}{t} = \frac{\ln\left(\dfrac{590}{373}\right)}{4}(100) = 11.5\% / \text{yr}$$

Interpretation of the curve indicates:

$D = 11.5\%/\text{yr}$ and $q_i = 590$ STB/month = 19.4 STB/D.

Calculate the reservoir pore volume. Use Eq. 4.14. Note the inclusion of the time conversion of months to years to cancel the production rate and decline rate time units.

$$V_p = \phi h A = \frac{5.615 q_i B}{D c_t \left(p_i - p_{wf}\right)}$$

$$V_p = \phi h A = \frac{5.615(590)(1.25)(12 \text{ months/yr})}{(0.115)(15 \times 10^{-6})(2,100 - 0)} = 13.718 \times 10^6 \text{ rcf}$$

Calculate the drainage area. The answer is generally more meaningful if expressed in acres. The porosity-thickness terms and the 43,560 ft^2/acre conversion expression are included to calculate the drainage area.

$$A = \frac{V_p}{\phi h} = \frac{13.718 \times 10^6}{(0.15)(42)(43,560)} = 50 \text{ acres}$$

Calculate the radius of drainage.

$$r_e = \left[\frac{50(43,560)}{\pi}\right]^{0.5} = 833 \text{ ft}$$

The calculated 50-acre drainage area is reasonably similar to the assumed 40-acre well-spacing value for the field.

Apply Eq. 4.15 to calculate average reservoir permeability.

$$k = \frac{141.2 q B \mu \left[\ln\left(\dfrac{r_e}{r_w}\right) - \dfrac{3}{4} + S\right]}{h\left(p_i - p_{wf}\right)}$$

$$k = \frac{141.2(19.4)(1.25)(1)\left[\ln\left(\dfrac{833}{0.33}\right) - \dfrac{3}{4}\right]}{(42)(2,100 - 0)} = 0.275 \text{ md}$$

How long does it take for the reservoir to attain boundary-dominated flow conditions? Apply Eq. 1.45.

$$t_{pss} \approx \frac{40 \phi \mu c_t r_e^2}{k}$$

$$t_{pss} \approx \frac{40(0.15)(1)(15 \times 10^{-6})(833)^2}{0.275} = 227 \text{ days}$$

The calculation indicates that it takes approximately 7.5 months for the reservoir to attain boundary-dominated flow conditions. The reservoir performance history shown in Fig. 4.7 appears to transition from transient- to boundary-dominated flow during the 10- to 12-month period.

More information about the field geology and general performance characteristics should be available before a quantitative estimate of the character of the well can truly be interpreted.

Chapter 5

The Hyperbolic Decline Curve

Fitting a polynomial equation to a rate-time curve approximates the production history with the equation of a line. In some cases, the highest-power term in the equation exerts an increasingly dominant influence with elapsed time even though the value of the expression does not materially affect the shape of the historical curve match. Therefore, the curve unknowingly deviates from the expected performance in the predictive phase of the analysis in which there is no comparative reference. These irregularities can prevent a realistic performance prediction. On the other hand, applying a hyperbolic equation to fit the characteristics of the producing curve ensures that the matching and prediction phases of the analysis process are represented by a monotonically declining curve.

Discussion in Chapter 1 shows that the Arps (1945) definitions for the exponential and hyperbolic decline curves ultimately converge to zero. The special-case harmonic curve does not converge but is included in the Arps (1945) definitions to provide a limiting bound. Analyzing hyperbolic and harmonic rate-time histories presents a problem because of the continuously changing slope of the lines.

Cutler (1924) defined a curve-shifting approach to force a straightline fit of the production curve plotted on log-log paper. The graphical trial-and-error method assumes that the coefficients defining the hyperbolic curve can be fitted to a straight line. The equation for the plot is as follows:

$$q = mt^b + C. \dotfill (5.1)$$

Estimating the correct curve coefficients from a log-log plot is somewhat problematic because of the compressed nature of the scales. The technique is useful, but the results of the analysis should be viewed as highly suspect. Better methods are available.

Slider (1968) constructed type curves on transparent overlays for exponent values in the range $0 \leq b \leq 1$. Selected dimensionless rate and cumulative production groups permitted applying the type-curve analysis method to a wide variety of conditions. Curves were presented to determine future producing rates and cumulative production after achieving the initial match. The technique is somewhat laborious but did simplify to a certain extent the tedious task of analyzing hyperbolic and harmonic decline curves.

These early methods were somewhat cumbersome and complicated, and consequently never generated wide appeal. Therefore, before the advent of personal computers and type curves, few people went through the process of finding the proper coefficients when analyzing a hyperbolic or harmonic decline.

The most straightforward analysis process divides the semilog rate-time plot into a series of straight lines of decreasing slope. Theoretically, the last straight line forms the basis for projecting future performance to the EL. **Fig. 5.1** illustrates the slopes of a successive straightline method analyzing the Redfish Point (Vermilion Parish, Louisiana) example problem.

In actual practice, the projection into the future is a combination of the slope of the last straight line coupled with knowledge of the average well history in the area. The selection process is a function of the skill and judgment of the interpreter and not based on any particular mathematical model. Some of the considerations that must be included in the selected and last decline rate are as follows:

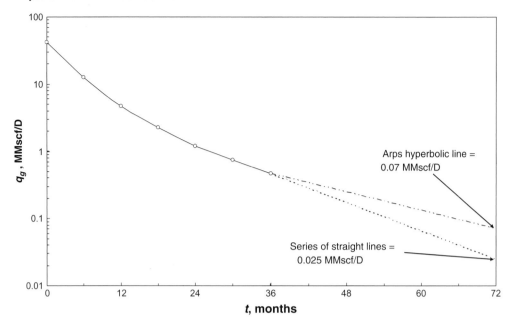

Fig. 5.1—Illustrating the series-of-straight-lines approach to approximate the Redfish Point well history. The series of approaches indicate that q = 0.025 MMscf/D at 72 months. Application of the Arps equation of a line method indicates q = 0.07 MMscf/D at 72 months. With which method do you feel most comfortable?

- Average well life
- Average decline rate late in the life of surrounding and field wells
- Expected operational life of the production string and facilities

This type of projection can be fraught with error, unless one is aware of the practical limits of the forecast.

Problem. The utility of the series-of-straight-lines approach is illustrated with the Redfish Point hyperbolic decline example problem. The smoothed monthly performance history, listed in 6-month time intervals, is shown in **Table 5.1** (Columns 1 and 2) and **Fig. 5.1.** Apply the series-of-straight-lines approach to estimate the producing rate at 72 months.

TABLE 5.1—DATA AND RESULTS OF CALCULATIONS: REDFISH POINT WELL

Time (months)	Producing Rate (MMscf/D)	Yearly Decline Rate (%/yr)	Monthly Decline Rate (fraction/month)	1/D (months)	Predicted Rate (MMscf/D)
0	42.00	–	–	–	87.50
6	12.70	239	0.199	5.01	17.37
12	4.67	203	0.169	6.00	5.83
18	2.28	144	0.120	8.33	2.56
24	1.19	130	0.108	9.26	1.32
30	0.74	95	0.079	12.66	0.76
36	0.47	91	0.076	13.16	0.47
48			0.067		0.21
60			0.054		0.11
72			0.038		0.07

Solution. Assume that the production curve declines exponentially to draw a straight line between each data point. The moderating decline rates are shown in Column 3 of Table 5.1. The example calculation to determine the exponential decline rate for the month interval is shown in the following application of Eq. 1.12:

$$D = \ln\left(\frac{q_i}{q_2}\right) = \ln\left(\frac{42}{12.7}\right) = 1.196/6 \text{ months} = 0.199/\text{month}$$

$$D = (1.196/6 \text{ months})(2)(100) = 239.2\%/\text{yr}$$

Column 3 in Table 5.1 shows that the exponential decline changes from 239%/yr during the first 6-month period to 91%/yr for the last 6-month period of data (over the total production history of 36 months). The pronounced decline rates indicate that the production history is still operating in the more arcuate part of the hyperbolic curve, and extrapolating the last straightline projection to the EL should be viewed with caution. Extending this straight line to $t = 72$ months indicates $q = 0.025$ MMscf/D.

In actuality, the Arps and type-curve solution methods calculated $q = 0.07$ MMscf/D at 72 months. The straight line between the last historical rate and 72 months yields $D = 64$ %/yr. Which of these projections is correct? A reasonable estimate was not achieved for the series-of-straight-lines approach, because the historical data ended in the arcuate portion of the curve. Applying a hyperbolic curve to the data forced the slope of the curve to continue to decrease. Applying some type of late-time field decline rate would possibly result in a more representative approximation than the strictly mathematical interpretation. A much more accurate method is to apply the Arps concepts to solve the problem.

The following discussion develops and compares the Arps (1945) and Fetkovich (1980) type-curve solutions for the hyperbolic and harmonic decline curves. The general equation for a hyperbola forms the starting point for development of the Arps (1945) equations. Decline rate is a function of the producing rate, and the exponent varies over the range $0 < b < 1$ for the hyperbolic case. A special limiting case is the harmonic curve that forms the upper boundary for the Arps curves when $b = 1$. The shape of the harmonic curve remains constant, while the shape for the hyperbolic curve varies over the $0 < b < 1$ range. A hyperbola reverts to the special case of the exponential form when the decline rate remains constant. Excellent additional literature citations on the application of the hyperbolic decline relationship can be found in Brons (1963), Fetkovich et al. (1994), Jacob and Lohman (1952), Kelkar and Perez (1988), and Long and Davis (1988). The development work, presented in these references, is discussed in more detail in Chapter 6.

5.1 The Arps Hyperbolic Equation

The equation of a line contains two unknown coefficients (q_i and D_i) for the harmonic case and three (q_i, D_i, and b) for the hyperbolic case. These coefficients are determined by reforming the hyperbolic or harmonic equations to represent a straight line. An iterative procedure is used to calculate the coefficients from the slope and intercept values obtained from the straight line. The solution procedure is complicated, time-consuming, and applicable only when performed with an interactive computer program.

5.1.1 Determining the Coefficients. Substitution of the hyperbolic producing rate-decline rate relationship, Eq. 1.20, into the rate-time Eq. 1.9 results in Eq. 5.2, relating the decreasing decline rate as a function of time and *b*-exponent.

$$\frac{1}{D} = bt + \frac{1}{D_i} \dots\dots\dots\dots\dots\dots\dots\dots\dots\dots\dots\dots\dots\dots\dots\dots\dots\dots \quad (5.2)$$

The previous equation is presented in the form of an equation of a straight line. The components of the straightline equation are as follows:

y axis – plotting variable: $\dfrac{1}{D}$ .... (5.3)

x axis – plotting variable: t .... (5.4)

y intercept – outcome term: $\dfrac{1}{D_i}$ .... (5.5)

Slope of line – outcome term: b .... (5.6)

A $1/D$ vs. t plot divides the production history into a series of panels with each panel representing the time required for the rate to decline from some early rate, q_1, to a later rate, q_2. The D_i and b coefficients are derived from the slope and intercept values of the $1/D$ vs. t graphical analysis. These two values are input into a rearranged form of Eq. 1.9 to solve for the initial production rate. The time interval applied to the solution is usually assumed to be the time elapsed between the start of production and the last historical production rate.

5.1.2 Analysis Procedure. The general analysis procedure begins by constructing a data plot to determine the three coefficients defining the hyperbolic curve. Measure the quality of the curve fit by comparing the shape and similarity of the historical and calculated producing rate curves. Apply the equation of the line to predict future performance as the last part of the analysis procedure. The following presents a more detailed description:

Plot the production data. The first part of the analysis constructs a semilog rate-time plot and smoothes the curve. Use the smoothed production decline curve to list the producing rates.

Find the coefficients defining the hyperbolic curve. Apply Eq. 1.12 to calculate the continuous decline rate for each time interval:

$$D = \dfrac{\ln\left(\dfrac{q_1}{q_2}\right)}{t}.$$

Construct a $1/D$ vs. t plot, and draw a best-fit straight line through the data points. Include the interpreted intercept and slope values into Eqs. 5.5 and 5.6 to calculate the initial decline rate and exponent. Two of the three unknown terms defining the hyperbolic rate-time equation are determined from this interpretation. However, the initial producing rate is still unknown.

Rearrange Eq. 1.9 to the following form to calculate the initial producing rate:

$$q_i = q_2\left(1 + bD_i t\right)^{\frac{1}{b}}. \quad .... (5.7)$$

The time interval t is usually defined as the time difference between initial production and the last historical data point. The initial point forms the starting point for the hyperbolic curve and does not necessarily possess any physical meaning. Any similarity of the field and calculated initial producing rates is simply a fortuitous circumstance. The three coefficients defining the hyperbolic curve have now been developed. The next and probably most important step determines the quality of the curve approximation.

Compare the calculated rates to the historical production rates. Include the previously determined coefficients and historical time periods into the hyperbolic rate equation, shown as Eq. 1.9, to calculate the production rates.

Plot the calculated rate values on the historical rate-time figure and compare the two curves. A match of a single data point is not a sufficient justification to verify the similarity of the hyperbolic equation to the performance curve. The hyperbola representing the complete set of calculated rate values must be compared to the historical curve. The curves should present similar slopes and character, which is a particularly important consideration when matching the late-time (boundary-dominated flow) production history, because the future performance character should be more similar to the late-time behavior, as compared to early-time production behavior. For the case in which the shapes of the field and calculated curves are not the same, the match with the best agreement with the late-time production history is favored.

Re-evaluate the fit of the straight line in the data plot if the character of the calculated and historical production data is judged dissimilar. Changing the slope and intercept of the data plot changes the three coefficients defining the hyperbola. Follow the same comparison to determine if the new coefficients improve the match between the historical and calculated rates. Experience has shown that this iterative process is very laborious and time-consuming. What often appears to be a slight adjustment to one of the coefficients may profoundly influence the shape of the hyperbolic curve. A statistical best fit does not necessarily produce the best equation of the hyperbola.

Calculate future performance. Apply Eqs. 1.9, 1.19, and 1.22 to calculate producing rate, elapsed time, and cumulative production. Refer to Table 1.1 for the appropriate equations.

Problem: Arps Approach. The curved semilog rate-time of plot for the Redfish Point No. 2 well shown in **Fig. 5.2** reflects a hyperbolic type performance history. The smoothed performance history and calculation procedure are listed in Table 5.1. Apply the Arps (1945) interpretation concepts to answer the following questions.

Estimate cumulative production expected over the 36- to 60-month period. How long does the well produce within the EL range of 60 to 90 Mscf/D?

Solution. Divide the performance history into a series of constant time steps to determine the coefficients defining the hyperbolic curve. Any time interval is appropriate as long as the units remain constant throughout the calculation procedure. Set up a table, such as seen in Table 5.1, and enter the rate values selected from the curve at each time interval. Columns 1 and 2 represent the smoothed time-rate data credited to the end of the historical record at month 36. The predictive portion of the table includes months 48, 60, and 72. Apply Eq. 1.12 to calculate the exponential decline rate for each interval. The example calculation for the first time step is shown as follows:

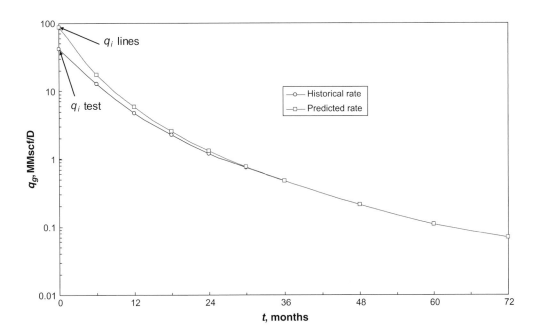

Fig. 5.2—Production decline curve for the Redfish Point Well 2. There is a reasonably good match between the historical and calculated data at mid- to late time.

$$D = \frac{\ln\left(\dfrac{q_1}{q_2}\right)}{t} = \frac{\ln\left(\dfrac{42}{12.7}\right)}{(6 \text{ months})} = 0.199/\text{month}$$

Note: The decline rate is expressed in fraction per month. Converting the time to a monthly basis simplifies the calculation procedure to a certain extent.

Construct the data plot. The inverse values of the instantaneous decline rate for each time interval are listed in Column 5 of Table 5.1. The $1/D$-time plot is shown in **Fig. 5.3.** The slope of the best-fit straight line is the exponent of the hyperbolic curve, while the intercept on the y axis represents the inverse of the initial decline rate (Eqs. 5.5 and 5.6). The following calculations illustrate the interpretation procedure:

$$\text{Slope, } b = \frac{y_2 - y_1}{x_2 - x_1} = \frac{9.86 - 8.10}{24 - 18} = 0.293$$

Intercept, $1/D_i = 2.90$ months, $D_i = 0.345/\text{month}$.

Apply the rearranged form of the rate equation, shown as Eq. 5.7, to calculate the initial flow rate. Production was assumed to have started 36 months before the last recorded rate.

$$q_i = q_2\left(1 + bD_i t\right)^{\frac{1}{b}} = (0.47)\left[1 + (0.293)(0.345)(36)\right]^{\frac{1}{0.293}} = 88.4 \text{ MMscf/D}$$

Note: The initial rate calculated by the fitted hyperbolic equation and the test rate of 42 MMscf/D are not the same. What caused this disparity? The 88.4-MMscf/D estimate is the starting point of the hyperbola, while the 42 MMscf/D represents the historical test data. This difference suggests that the historical data cannot be represented by a single hyperbolic equation. The analysis procedure indicates that the hyperbolic coefficients replicating the performance curve of the Redfish Point well are $D_i = 0.345/\text{month}$, $q_i = 88.4$ MMscf/D, and $b = 0.293$.

Compare the calculated to the historical data. This is the most critical step in the entire calculation procedure. Apply Eq. 1.9 to calculate the production rate at each period to compare with the historical data. The quality of the prediction is based on the "goodness" of the fit. The following illustrates the calculation to determine the rate at the end of the first 12-month period.

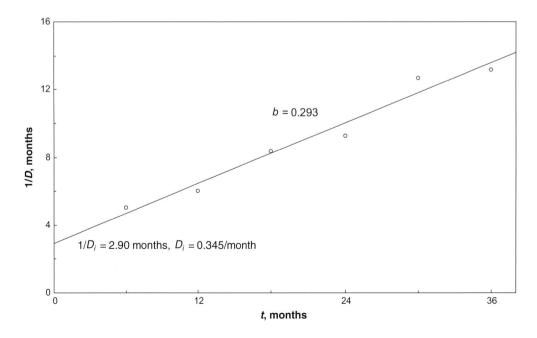

Fig. 5.3—Interpretation of the reciprocal decline rate-time plot for the Redfish Point well.

$$q_2 = \frac{q_i}{\left(1 + bD_i t\right)^{\frac{1}{b}}} = \frac{88.4}{\left[1 + (0.293)(0.345)(12)\right]^{\frac{1}{0.293}}} = 5.88 \text{ MMscf/D}$$

Fig. 5.2 shows that the theoretical hyperbolic curve compares favorably to the historical well test curve at mid- to late-time. There is a good degree of parallelism between the two during most of the history. Therefore, select the modeled hyperbolic curve as the correct curve for predicting performance. The calculated rates are listed in Column 6 of Table 5.1.

For this particular case, the initial interpretation of the hyperbolic coefficients produced a hyperbola that adequately modeled the performance curve. Therefore, other iterations to find more comparable coefficients were not required. One seldom experiences such a fortuitous first-time solution in real life.

Calculate cumulative production expected during the 36- to 60-month period. The decline and producing rate information are obtained from Table 5.1. Eq. 1.22 calculates the cumulative production between successive times. The first rate was chosen to be at 36 months and the last rate at 60 months for this case. Note: The conversion factor used to equalize the difference between the flow rate in units of MMscf/D with the decline rate expressed in fracture/month units.

$$G_p = \frac{q_i}{D_i\left(1 - b\right)}\left[1 - \left(\frac{q_2}{q_i}\right)^{1-b}\right]$$

$$G_p = \frac{(0.47)(30.4375 \text{ days/month})}{(0.076/\text{month})(1 - 0.293)}\left[1 - \left(\frac{0.11}{0.47}\right)^{1-0.293}\right] = 171 \text{ MMscf}$$

Calculate time interval encompassing the 60- to 90-Mscf/D rate decline. The problem can be solved by two methods. One method is to extend the rate-time curve shown in Fig. 5.2 outward, and then read the time at which the curve declined to that particular rate. The other method applies the time equation shown as Eq. 1.19.

The time required for the producing rate to decline from initial conditions to 90 Mscf/D (0.09 MMscf/D) is as follows:

$$t = \frac{\left(\frac{q_i}{q_2}\right)^b - 1}{bD_i} = \frac{\left(\frac{88.4}{0.09}\right)^{0.293} - 1}{(0.293)(0.345)} = 64.6 \text{ months}$$

The time required for the producing rate to decline from initial conditions to 60 Mscf/D (0.06 MMscf/D) is as follows:

$$t = \frac{\left(\frac{q_i}{q_2}\right)^b - 1}{bD_i} = \frac{\left(\frac{88.4}{0.06}\right)^{0.293} - 1}{(0.293)(0.345)} = 74 \text{ months}$$

$\Delta t = 74 - 64.6 = 9.4$ months

Subtraction of the two values indicates there is a 9- to 10-month period in which the well produces within the EL range of 60 to 90 Mscf/D. The lower limit on the EL range is 60 Mscf/D (0.06 MMscf/D), which is reached in 74 months. The upper range for the EL flow rate is 90 Mscf/D (0.09 MMscf/D), which is reached in 64.6 months. Therefore, for a production time between 64.6 to 74 months, the well is operating under marginal economics. The point at which the decision is made to cease production operations of the well is selected based on the actual economics of the well operation during this period.

Problem: Type-Curve Approach. Apply the Fetkovich type-curve approach to calculate the volume of oil expected to be produced during the 36- to 48-month period from Redfish Point Well 2.

The rate-time data are listed in Table 5.1, while the hyperbolic equations are summarized in Table 1.1. The overlay of the rate-time data and the Fetkovich type curve is shown in **Fig. 5.4.** Determine the following:

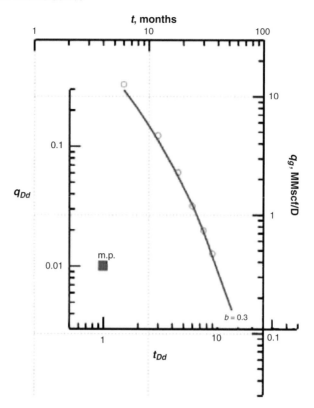

Fig. 5.4—Type-curve match for the Redfish Point well. Dimensionless and field rate and time relationships are determined at the selected match point.

- Initial producing and decline rates and exponent values
- Producing rate at 48 months
- Cumulative production for the 36- to 48-month interval
- Length of time for well to produce within the EL range of 60 to 90 Mscf/D.

Solution. Overlay the log-log plot on the Fetkovich type curve and obtain a curve fit. A type-curve match is achieved with the $b = 0.3$ curve. An equally good fit can be obtained with the $b = 0.4$ and $b = 0.5$ stems. However, selection of any of these stems does not materially affect the quality of the results.

Match points: $b = 0.3$, $t_{Dd} = 1$, $q_{Dd} = 0.01$, $t = 3.9$ months, $q = 0.45$ MMscf/D

Calculate the initial producing rate and initial decline rate. Apply Eqs. 1.31 and 1.32.

$$q_i = \frac{q}{q_{Dd}} = \frac{0.45}{0.01} = 45 \text{ MMscf/D}$$

$$D_i = \frac{t_{Dd}}{t} = \frac{1}{3.9} = 0.256/\text{month}$$

Determine initial time. Coincidentally, the last recorded rate of 0.47 MMscf/D after 36 months of production merges with the Arps $b = 0.3$ stem. Apply Eq. 1.19 to calculate the interval between present and initial time when $q_i = 45$ MMscf/D.

$$t = \frac{\left(\dfrac{q_i}{q_2}\right)^b - 1}{bD_i} = \frac{\left(\dfrac{45}{0.47}\right)^{0.3} - 1}{(0.3)(0.256)} = 38.1 \text{ months}$$

The producing rate at 48 months. Extend the field rate along the type curve to 48 months to find q at 48 months = 0.22 MMscf/D.

Cumulative production from the 36 to 48 months. Recall Eq. 1.21:

$$G_p = \frac{q_i}{D_i(1-b)}\left[1 - \left(\frac{q_2}{q_i}\right)^{1-b}\right]$$

At $t = 36$ months:

$$G_p = \frac{45(30.4375\ \text{days/month})}{(0.256/\text{month})(1-0.3)}\left[1 - \left(\frac{0.47}{45}\right)^{1-0.3}\right] = 7,330\ \text{MMscf}$$

At $t = 48$ months:

$$G_p = \frac{45(30.4375\ \text{days/month})}{(0.256/\text{month})(1-0.3)}\left[1 - \left(\frac{0.22}{45}\right)^{1-0.3}\right] = 7,459\ \text{MMscf}$$

ΔG_p between 36 and 48 months = 7,459 MMscf to 7,330 MMscf = 129 MMscf

Another method is to use Eq. 1.21 and assume that initial time is at 36 months. Table 5.1 indicates D at 36 months = 7.6%/month.

$$G_p = \frac{q_i}{D_i(1-b)}\left[1 - \left(\frac{q_2}{q_i}\right)^{1-b}\right]$$

$$G_p = \frac{(0.47)(30.4375\ \text{days/month})}{(0.076/\text{month})(1-0.3)}\left[1 - \left(\frac{0.22}{0.47}\right)^{1-0.3}\right] = 111\ \text{MMscf}$$

There is only a small difference between the two answers, although the first method should be the more accurate of the two.

Table 5.2 compares the results of the conventional and type-curve analysis of Redfish Point Well 2. There is a considerable disparity in the initial decline and producing rate values. However, there are only minor differences between the cumulative recovery estimates, which are of the most interest.

5.2 The Harmonic Equation
The Arps (1945) solution for approximating the equation of the harmonic curve is somewhat easier than the procedure for analyzing the general hyperbolic curve, because only the initial rate and decline rate coefficients form the equation coefficients. The exponent remains constant at $b = 1$.

5.2.1 Determining the Coefficients. Rearrange the rate-time relationship (Eq. 1.25) for the harmonic curve to the following form:

$$\frac{1}{q} = \frac{1}{q_i} + \frac{D_i t}{q_i}. \qquad \dots\dots\dots\dots\dots\dots\dots\dots\dots\dots\dots\dots\dots\dots\dots\dots\dots\dots\dots \quad (5.8)$$

TABLE 5.2—COMPARISON OF COEFFICIENTS: REDFISH POINT WELL		
Parameter	Type Curve	Arps Conventional
b exponent	0.3	0.293
q_i, MMscf/D	45	88.4
D_i, fraction/month	0.256	0.345
$G_{p(36-48\ \text{months})}$, Bscf	0.129	0.115

Applying the equation of a straight line to Eq. 5.8 results in the following components of the line:

$$y \text{ axis} - \text{plotting variable:} \frac{1}{q}. \quad \dots\dots\dots\dots\dots\dots\dots\dots\dots\dots\dots\dots \quad (5.9)$$

$$x \text{ axis} - \text{plotting variable:} \ t. \quad \dots\dots\dots\dots\dots\dots\dots\dots\dots\dots\dots\dots\dots \quad (5.10)$$

$$y \text{ intercept} - \text{outcome term:} \frac{1}{q_i}. \quad \dots\dots\dots\dots\dots\dots\dots\dots\dots\dots\dots \quad (5.11)$$

$$\text{Slope of line} - \text{outcome term:} \frac{D_i}{q_i}. \quad \dots\dots\dots\dots\dots\dots\dots\dots\dots\dots\dots \quad (5.12)$$

The input terms are the known rate and time values, while the outcome terms are the sought-after initial producing rate and decline rate. The intercept and slope values of the straight line determine the q_i and D_i coefficients defining the shape of the harmonic curve. The quality of the coefficients obtained from the data plot analysis can only be determined by comparing the predicted producing rate to the historical values. Oftentimes, an extended trial-and-error solution is required.

5.2.2 Analysis Procedure. Interpret producing rates and calculate equivalent $1/q$ values from a smoothed production decline curve. Draw a best-fit straight line through the data points on a $1/q$ vs. time plot. The slope and intercept values are coupled with Eqs. 5.11 and 5.12 to calculate q_i and D_i.

Determine the "goodness" of calculated history. Apply the rate-time, Eq. 1.25, to compare the calculated rate data with the field data to determine the "goodness" of the coefficients. Re-evaluate the straightline fit of the data if the calculated and historical production curves are dissimilar. Matching of medium- to late-time data is much more important than matching the early-time data.

Predict performance. Apply Eqs. 1.25, 1.26, and 1.27 to calculate future production characteristics of the harmonic decline curve after determining the proper coefficients.

Problem: Arps Approach. Valentine Well 2 is expected to exhibit a harmonic production decline because the producing interval is composed of three differing permeability layers. **Table 5.3** lists the production data and the results of the calculations, while **Fig. 5.5** illustrates the performance history and the match between historical and calculated rates. The operator wishes to determine the following information:

- Calculate the volume of oil expected to be produced during the 36- to 60-month period.
- Determine length of time for the rate to decline to 50 bbl of oil per month (BOPM).
- Verify that the decline curve reflects a harmonic equation.

Solution. Calculate the initializing coefficients for the Valentine harmonic decline curve. The inverse rate values required for the data plot are listed in Table 5.3, while the data plot is shown in **Fig. 5.6.**

Combine the intercept and slope values obtained from the straightline interpretation of the data plot with Eqs. 5.11 and 5.12 to calculate the q_i and D_i coefficients.

$$\text{Intercept value} = \frac{1}{q_i} = 0.000241 \text{ months/STB, or } q_i = 4{,}149 \text{ STB/month.}$$

$$\text{Slope} = \frac{D_i}{q_i} = 0.000205 / \text{STB.}$$

$$D_i = q_i(\text{Slope}) = (4{,}149)(0.000205) = 0.85/\text{month.}$$

Check the "goodness" of the coefficients. Apply the rate-time relationship (Eq. 1.25) to check the "goodness" of the coefficients calculated from the data plot. The following is the rate calculation for the 36-month period:

TABLE 5.3—DATA AND RESULTS OF CALCULATIONS: VALENTINE WELL 2				
Time (months)	Rate (STB/month)	$1/q$ (month/STB)	Match (STB/month)	N_p (STB)
0	–	–	4,149	0
1	2,620	0.0004	2,243	2,620
2	1,690	0.0006	1,537	4,310
4	920	0.0011	943	6,390
6	695	0.0014	680	7,945
8	574	0.0017	532	9,082
10	409	0.0025	437	9,972
12	379	0.0026	371	10,729
14	316	0.0032	322	11,399
16	245	0.0041	284	11,930
18	248	0.0040	255	12,460
20	236	0.0042	231	12,939
22	217	0.0046	211	13,356
24	209	0.0048	194	13,758
26	187	0.0054	180	14,123
28	168	0.0060	167	14,470
30	151	0.0066	157	14,784
32	152	0.0066	147	15,092
34	139	0.0072	139	15,377
36	128	0.0078	131	16,638
48	–	–	99	–
60	–	–	80	18,030

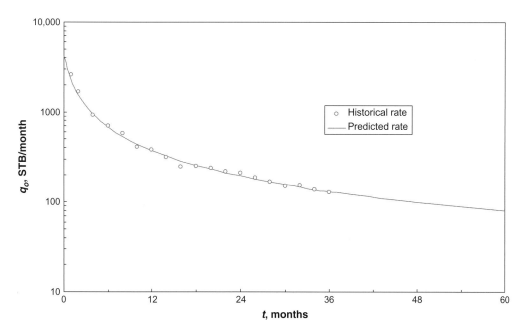

Fig. 5.5—The historical and predicted rate-time plot, Valentine Well 2. Note the quality of the curve fit to the historical data.

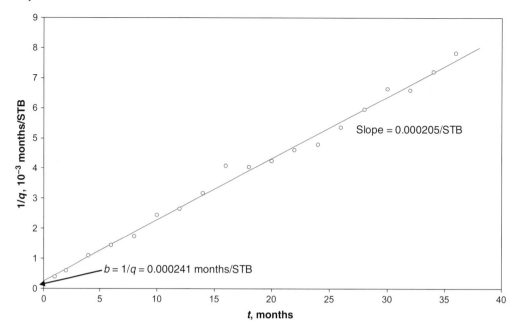

Fig. 5.6—The data plot, Valentine Well 2.

$$q = \frac{q_i}{1 + D_i t} = \frac{4{,}149}{1 + (0.85)(36)} = 131 \text{ STB/month.}$$

The calculated rate of 131 STB/month compares favorably with the historical 128-STB/month producing rate of the well. However, the complete rate history must be matched with the calculated values to compare the similarity of the curves. Single-valued comparisons do not furnish sufficient proof. A complete history match of the rate data is shown in Table 5.3 and Fig. 5.5. Note: There is a degree of parallelism and excellent match between the historical and calculated rate values. Rate predictions for 48 and 60 months are also listed in the table.

Determine the cumulative production between 36 and 60 months. The first issue is to determine q at 60 months and D at 36 months for input into the cumulative production equation. Use the rate equation (Eq. 1.25) to calculate the production rate at 60 months.

$$q_2 = \frac{q_i}{1 + D_i t} = \frac{4{,}149}{1 + (0.85)(60)} = 79.8 \text{ STB/month}$$

Apply a revised version of Eq. 1.24 to calculate the decline rate at 36 months.

$$D_{36 \text{ months}} = \frac{q_{36 \text{ months}} D_i}{q_i} = \frac{(131)(0.85)}{4{,}149} = 0.027 / \text{month}$$

Use Eq. 1.28 to determine cumulative production spanning the 36- through 60-month period.

$$Q_p = \frac{q_{36 \text{ months}}}{D_{36 \text{ months}}} \ln\left(\frac{q_{60 \text{ months}}}{q_{36 \text{ months}}}\right) = \frac{131}{0.027} \ln\left(\frac{131}{79.8}\right) = 2{,}404 \text{ STB}$$

How long will it take for the rate to decline to 50 STB/D? One method would be to apply the rate equation (Eq. 1.25) to calculate a series of future rates and draw a smooth line along the plot. Any rate-time prediction can be generated by interpolating along the curve. An alternate method applies Eq. 1.26 to calculate the time for the production to decline from initial conditions to the 50-STB/D limit.

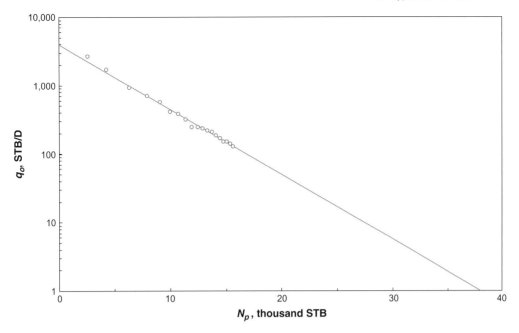

Fig. 5.7—The semilogarithmic cumulative production plot, Valentine Well 2. The straightline trend of the data verifies the harmonic nature of the curve.

$$t = \frac{q_i - q_2}{D_i q} = \frac{4{,}149 - 50}{(0.85)(50)} = 96.4 \ \text{months}$$

Verify that the decline curve reflects a harmonic equation. Table 5.3 lists the cumulative production, while **Fig. 5.7** presents the plot of the data. A reasonable straightline fit is evident. The production decline curve of the Valentine well appears to be harmonic.

Problem: Type-Curve Approach. Apply the Fetkovich type-curve approach to calculate the volume of oil expected to be produced during the 36- to 60-month period from Valentine Well 2. The well-producing history is expected to display harmonic decline characteristics. The rate-time data are listed in Table 5.3, while the harmonic equations are shown in Table 1.1. **Fig. 5.8** presents the overlay of the rate-time data and the type curve. Use the type-curve approach to calculate the following:

- Determine the initial producing rate and decline rate values.
- Calculate the cumulative production expected during the 36- to 60-month period.
- Determine length of time for the well to decline to 50 STB/month?

Overlay the log-log plot on the Fetkovich type curve and obtain a match. The best match was chosen at $b = 1$. In actuality, a match of $b = 0.9$ appears to be equally good. The following set of match points was obtained for the $b = 1$ curve overlay:

Match points: $t_{Dd} = 10$, $q_{Dd} = 0.1$, $t = 6.9$ months, $q = 720$ STB/month.

Calculate the initial producing rate and initial decline rate. Apply Eqs. 1.31 and 1.32 to calculate the initial producing and decline rates.

$$D_i = \frac{t_{Dd}}{t} = \frac{10}{6.9} = 1.45/\text{month}$$

$$q_i = \frac{q}{q_{Dd}} = \frac{720}{0.1} = 7{,}200 \ \text{STB/month}$$

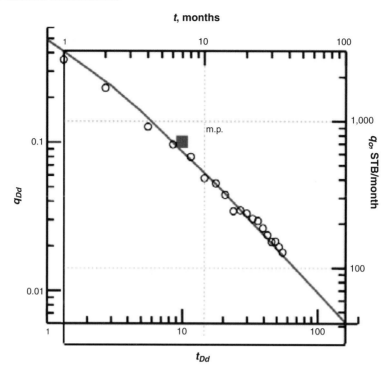

Fig. 5.8—Field and type-curve match for the Valentine Well 2 harmonic decline example.

Calculate cumulative production during the 36- to 60-month time period. Extrapolate the field data downward along the type curve to find the producing rate expected at the 36- and 60-month periods.

By inspection, q at 36 months = 130 STB/month, and q at 60 months = 79 STB/month

Apply Eq. 1.28 to calculate cumulative recovery for the harmonic decline curve.

$$Q_p = \frac{q_i}{D_i} \ln\left(\frac{q_i}{q}\right) = \frac{7,200}{1.45} \ln\left(\frac{7,200}{130}\right) = 19,933 \text{ STB}$$

$$Q_p = \frac{q_i}{D_i} \ln\left(\frac{q_i}{q}\right) = \frac{7,200}{1.45} \ln\left(\frac{7,200}{79}\right) = 22,406 \text{ STB}$$

Incremental cumulative production = 2,473 STB.

How long will it take for the well to decline to 50 STB/month? Extend the curve match until q = 50 STB/month at t = 94 months.

These values are compared to the conventional Arps analysis method in **Table 5.4.** The incremental cumulative production results are essentially the same. Perhaps the type-curve approach is easier.

TABLE 5.4—COMPARISON OF COEFFICIENTS: VALENTINE WELL		
Parameter	Type Curve	Arps Conventional
q_i, STB/month	7,200	4,149
D_i, fraction/month	1.45	0.85
$N_{p(36-60 \text{ months})}$, STB	2,473	2,404

The Arps rate-time relationships are based on the assumption that the b-exponent term is never greater than unity. Unfortunately, there are any number of case-history examples in which a good curve fit may be achieved with Eq. 1.9 for $b > 1$ values. This phenomenon is quite prevalent when studying the performance history of highly-variable-permeability, layered, and naturally fractured reservoirs where the matrix permeability is very low, often measured in microdarcies (1 μd = 1 × 10^{-6} D = 0.001 md). The large exponent values are the product of long-lived crossflow from very-low-permeability zones to high-permeability conduits feeding to the wellbore.

Chapter 6

Interpretation of Field Curves

Discussion in Chapter 1 showed that the solution to the diffusivity equation for single-phase flow of a slightly compressible fluid from a bounded reservoir case can model an exponential production decline curve. Therefore, an exponential decline reflects pressure-depletion conditions of a single-phase fluid.

Deviation of a production decline curve from the exponential form may be caused by the following:

- The presence of transient conditions in the case when the reservoir appears to be infinite in size
- The influence of water influx and gas cap expansion drive mechanisms during the depletion process
- The effect of changing compressibility and mobility of the produced fluids in the reservoir system
- An initial secondary fluid becoming predominant in the producing stream (an oil well gradually changing to a very high GOR is an example of the predominantly produced fluid changing from oil to gas)

Water influx for oil and gas reservoirs and gas-cap formation and expansion for oil reservoirs add energy to the reservoir. Conservation of reservoir pressure reduces the rate of production decline. Fig. 2.4 illustrates that extrapolating early-time production decline into the future can result in an erroneously high reserves estimate. The onset of water production beginning at 32 months caused a dramatic decline in production rate and eventual well abandonment. Decline-curve analysis should not be conducted for reservoirs suspected of being influenced by external drive mechanisms.

As a rule-of-thumb, predicting reservoir performance with any degree of certainty cannot be accomplished until at least 10% of the reserves have been produced. In most instances, external drive mechanisms and changing compressibility, relative-permeability, and fluid effects affect the production curve only after a reasonable pressure drop and elapsed time interval occur. Extrapolation of early-time data into the future can result in either an underestimation or overestimation of reserves.

The following section discusses how reservoir heterogeneity and changing system compressibility and mobility can influence the shape of a production decline curve. Two-phase flow effects on well performance are discussed in Chapter 7.

6.1 Transient and Transition Flow

An exponential decline reflects single-phase flow from a homogeneous-producing interval located in a bounded reservoir. As a rule, one may say that the presence of $b > 0.6$ usually reflects the dominance of transient conditions defining the shape of the decline curve. Transient flow can be exhibited when production is from the following:

- An infinite-acting, homogeneous reservoir. This phenomenon is rarely observed except in short-term production tests, and normal decline-curve analysis methods are seldom applied for this case.
- A layered or fractured reservoir in which there is a significant permeability contrast between the various flow branches within the producing system.

Transient conditions imply never-ending production. Type curves to interpret decline curves experiencing transient conditions were developed by Jacob and Lohman (1952). However, transient conditions do not last for an infinite period of time, and all reservoirs eventually experience boundary-dominated flow.

6.1.1 The Effect of Layering. Eq. 1.44 relates the time required for a reservoir to transition from infinite-acting to boundary-dominated flow conditions. The permeability term located in the denominator indicates that a more permeable layer of a noncommunicating, multizone completion enters boundary-dominated depletion conditions within a shorter length of time than would occur for a less permeable member.

Commingled production at the wellbore of a noncommunicating, layered reservoir system presents a combination of bounded and transient conditions in which amalgam is a transient curve of ill-defined shape. The combination of the different flow regimes often results in a decline behavior exhibiting an exponent value ranging over $0.8 < b < 1$. In actuality, the b-exponent term can exhibit b values greater than 1. Layered or fractured reservoirs with moderate-to-high-permeability flow branches may act as a homogeneous system, while reservoirs with some combination of very-low- and very-high-permeability flow branches may remain in the infinite-acting mode until the well declines to the EL. As a rule, the longevity of transient conditions is reduced as the degree of crossflow between the various flow branches within the system increases.

Boundary conditions defining the possible range of production decline characteristics of layered or fractured, pressure-depleting reservoirs are (a) homogeneous-acting when the completion interval is composed of a multiplicity of layers of widely differing permeabilities, and the effects of crossflow are significant (the shape of the production decline curve is smoothly declining and appears as a continuous transition from transient to pseudosteady-state conditions), and (b) heterogeneous-acting when the completion interval contains a few productive layers, each possessing a distinctively different permeability, and there is no crossflow. The production curve declines as a series of steplike changes defined by the time for each layer to enter pseudosteady-state conditions.

Gentry and McCray (1978) studied the effect of reservoir heterogeneity on the shape of the production decline curve producing from an oil reservoir with a computer simulation model. Layers ranging from homogeneous to highly heterogeneous were included in the study. The producing intervals, listed in order of increasing degree of heterogeneity, were as follows:

- Homogeneous case: A single 1-millidarcy (md) permeability layer.
- H1 case: Three zones that comprise the most homogeneous of the three heterogeneous cases. Two of the zones display widely contrasting permeabilities. The third zone contains layers common to the two contrasting zones. The effect of the permeability distribution was to create a rather homogeneous producing interval. L1(1+3), L2(3+9), L3(5+15), millidarcies.
- H2 case: Two zones. Each zone contains one layer of widely contrasting permeability and one layer containing essentially a common permeability. L1(1+5) , L2(3+15), millidarcies.
- H3 case: Two single-permeability zones. The most heterogeneous of the three cases. There is a 15-fold difference in the permeability. L1(1), L2(15), millidarcies.

The results of the depletion study are shown in **Fig. 6.1.** A homogeneous, 1-md-sand case was included to provide a basis for comparison. The homogeneous case exhibits a smoothly declining production decline curve.

The previous description of the cases shows the characteristics of three sample reservoirs of varying degrees of heterogeneity. The degree of complexity increases numerically, because H3 > H2 > H1. Increasing reservoir heterogeneity implies that transient conditions exist for a longer period. Fig. 6.1 shows that each of the three cases gradually trends to the homogeneous case because of the gradual conversion of each layer to boundary-dominated flow conditions.

Fig. 2.5 is an example of a dual-porosity, very-low-matrix-permeability, naturally fractured system. Matrix permeability is measured in terms of 0.001 md, and the fracture permeability is at least 1,000 times greater. Unloading the fractures and depleting the matrix oil very close to the fracture face defines the slope and shape of the early-time decline. However, the curve flattens out with time and reflects production from the matrix when the fractures simply act as conduits to the wellbore. Eventually, the production curve must exhibit an exponential decline when boundary-dominated conditions predominate.

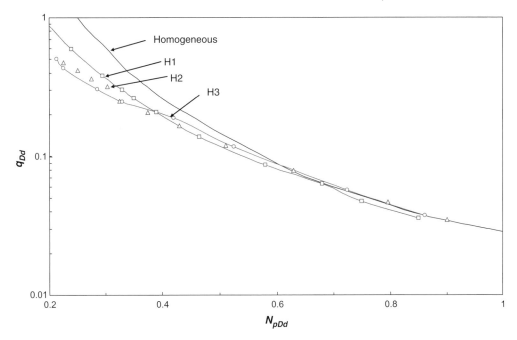

Fig. 6.1—Comparing rate response from reservoirs with varying degrees of heterogeneity (Gentry and McCray 1978). All heterogeneous reservoirs eventually trend to the uniform interval exponential decline case.

The uninitiated may use the early-time decline and underestimate ultimate recovery or extend the well life along the second, flat-lying transient curve to unreasonable lengths and overestimate reserves. In either case, the true value lies somewhere in between the two incorrect estimates. Reviewing reserves estimates for these reservoir types developed from the analysis of decline curves should be conducted with a great amount of caution and thought. An approximation method to calculate reserves for this type of producing system is discussed later in this chapter.

6.1.2 Compressibility and Relative-Permeability Effects. A production decline curve seldom displays a constant hyperbolic character throughout its life. The exponent value generally varies and decreases in value as the reservoir is depleted. Gentry and McCray (1978) coupled simulation and field studies to show that the exponent term generally decreases with declining reservoir pressure. The character of the reservoir rock, fluid properties, and degree of heterogeneity influences the b-exponent term. The results of the simulation studies were expressed as plots of dimensionless rate, time, and cumulative production groups defined as Eqs. 1.31 through 1.33.

A portion of the results of their studies is shown in **Fig. 6.2** for the No. 2 Typical Dolomite pressure-depletion case plotted on a semilog, dimensionless rate-time scale. Background curves for exponential, harmonic, and hyperbolic (i.e., $b = 0.5$) cases are included for reference. The sand thickness and relative-permeability curves remained constant for the 40-acre reservoir. The calculated decline curve follows the harmonic equation until $t_{Dd} = 5$, when there is a pronounced decline in the exponent value. The last two data points appear to indicate that the decline curve is following a hyperbolic $b = 0.4$ stem. Changing compressibility and relative-permeability values causes the exponent term to vary with production history.

Camacho-Velazquez (1987) and Camacho-Velazquez and Raghavan (1989) considered both a theoretical development and computer simulation to show how changing relative-permeability and fluid properties affect the shape of the decline curve. The following is a short review of their theoretical development.

Eq. 1.39 defines the van Everdingen and Hurst (1949) relationship between real and dimensionless time. The relationship holds true as long as the effective permeability, viscosity of the single-phase fluid, and compressibility of the system do not change appreciably. The viscosity and system compressibility terms should be evaluated within an integral with limits that are initial and final pressure for the equation to be theoretically correct. The effective permeability term is a function of the changing reservoir fluid-saturation values. These three reservoir parameters may exhibit a considerable change in value during the life of a pressure-depleting oil reservoir.

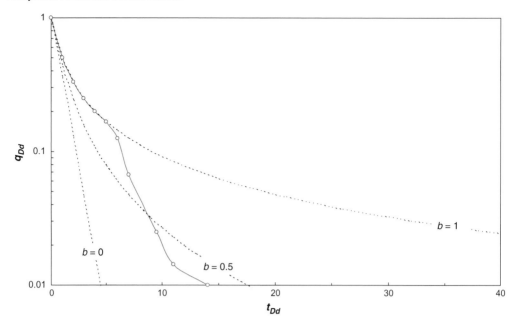

Fig. 6.2—A semilog rate-time plot illustrating the trend of the exponent value to smaller values for a pressure-depleting reservoir (Gentry and McCray 1978).

Camacho-Velazquez (1987) defined a more general expression for the real dimensionless-time relation. The rate, mobility, and compressibility values stationed inside the integral are a function of pressure and relative permeability. The t' term (parameter of integration) defines the time at which the average value of the property is obtained.

$$t_D^{\approx} = \frac{0.00633 k_a}{\phi r_w^2 q_o(t)_o} \int_0^t \frac{q_0(t')\bar{\lambda}_t(t')}{\bar{c}_t(t')} dt', \quad \dots\dots\dots\dots\dots\dots\dots\dots\dots\dots\dots\dots\dots\dots \quad (6.1)$$

where the system compressibility is a function of the weighted average oil, gas, and rock compressibilities in the reservoir, c_t; relative permeability effects, $\dfrac{k_{ro}}{\mu_o B_o}$; and system mobility, $\bar{\lambda}_t = \dfrac{k_{ro}}{\mu_o} + \dfrac{k_{rg}}{\mu_g}$.

The effect of changing system compressibility and relative-permeability values during the history of a typical pressure-depleting oil reservoir was investigated. **Fig. 6.3** illustrates the results of one of the Camacho-Velazquez and Raghavan (1989) depletion studies. Reservoir pressure declined from 1,600 to 200 psi.

The $\bar{c}_t/\bar{\lambda}_t$ term remains relatively constant at early time until an appreciable gas saturation has been established. Buildup of free gas saturation in the reservoir increases the system compressibility. However, excess gas production eventually depletes the reservoir of some of the free gas, and the $\bar{c}_t/\bar{\lambda}_t$ term decreases. It eventually attains a constant value when the reservoir pressure declines to a very low value and essentially constant system conditions are attained. Fig. 6.3 illustrates how the $\bar{c}_t/\bar{\lambda}_t$ term may vary by a factor of 10 during the life of a pressure depleting oil reservoir. The calculation of an average $\bar{c}_t/\bar{\lambda}_t$ value for the life of the reservoir appears to be nearly an impossible task because of the erratic nature of the track of the path. This study illustrates why the decline history of a pressure-depleting reservoir should be divided into producing segments if segmentation appears to be present. Determining an average curve for the complete well history may not necessarily represent a reasonable curve for extrapolating into the future.

Theoretical studies showed that the Muskat material balance equation and the constant pressure solution to the diffusivity equation can be expressed in the following form:

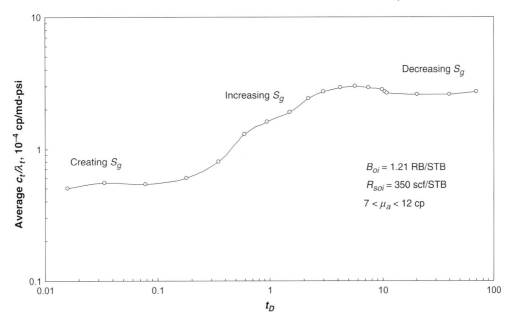

Fig. 6.3—Effect of changing gas saturation on the compressibility-mobility term (Camacho-Velazquez and Raghavan 1989).

$$\frac{dN_p}{d\bar{p}} = \frac{\bar{c}_t \alpha}{\bar{\lambda}_t} \frac{\phi Ah}{5.615}. \quad \dots\dots\dots\dots\dots\dots\dots\dots\dots\dots\dots\dots\dots\dots\dots\dots\dots\dots\dots\dots \quad (6.2)$$

Eq. 6.2 indicates that the relationship between cumulative production and pressure decline in a solution gas drive reservoir is a function of original oil-in-place, reservoir compressibility, and relative-permeability effects. In a practical sense, one would expect the relation between production and loss of pressure in a pressure-depleting reservoir to be controlled by reservoir fluid and rock properties and OOIP. Eq. 6.2 represents the base for developing Eq. 6.3.

$$\frac{D \ln q_0}{dt} = \frac{0.04 k_a}{\phi AC} \left(\frac{\bar{\lambda}_t}{\bar{c}_t} \right). \quad \dots\dots\dots\dots\dots\dots\dots\dots\dots\dots\dots\dots\dots\dots\dots\dots\dots\dots\dots \quad (6.3)$$

The term C is a dimensionless constant, defining the shape factor and skin characteristics, while D is the exponential decline rate. The equation implies that a straight line results from a semilog rate-time plot when the compressibility and mobility terms remain constant. This event holds true for single-phase flow of a slightly compressible fluid.

Eq. 6.3 reverts to an exponential form when the $\bar{c}_t / \bar{\lambda}_t$ term remains constant. All other terms are assumed to remain constant. The constant properties assumption holds true for single-phase flow conditions when only moderate changes in reservoir pressure occur. This condition occurs in oil reservoirs operating at or higher than the bubblepoint pressure and in very-high- or very-low-pressured gas reservoirs. Brons (1963) observed that these reservoir types display an exponential decline under constant BHFP conditions.

Eq. 6.4 defines the initial decline rate in terms of fluid and rock properties and reservoir size when the Arps equations are substituted into Eq. 6.3.

$$D_i = \frac{0.04 k_a}{\phi AC} \left(\frac{\bar{\lambda}_t}{\bar{c}_t} \right). \quad \dots\dots\dots\dots\dots\dots\dots\dots\dots\dots\dots\dots\dots\dots\dots\dots\dots\dots\dots\dots\dots \quad (6.4)$$

A rewritten form of Eq. 6.4 relates the Arps (1945) exponent value to the pressure-dependent compressibility and mobility effects.

$$b = -\frac{D\phi A}{0.04k_a}\frac{d}{dt}\left(\frac{\bar{c}_t}{\bar{\lambda}_t}\right). \dots\dots\dots\dots\dots\dots\dots\dots\dots\dots\dots\dots\dots\dots\dots\dots\dots \quad (6.5)$$

The value of the Arps (1945) exponent is a function of reservoir pore volume, effective permeability, and the average system compressibility and mobility values. Recall that the effective permeability, system compressibility, and mobility are assumed to remain constant in an exponential decline relationship. The extension of the constant flowing pressure, closed outer-boundary solution to the diffusivity equation by Camacho-Velazquez and Raghavan (1989) provided a fundamental understanding of the variables included in the Arps exponent term.

The effect of loss in pressure in a solution-gas-drive reservoir on the value of the Arps (1945) exponent term was studied with a reservoir simulator. A variety of conditions were considered by including different reservoir fluid and rock property data sets into the model. **Fig. 6.4** presents the simulated depletion history of Data Set 1. The figure was adapted from Camacho-Velazquez and Raghavan (1989), Fig. 6. The exponent term remained constant at $b = 1$ during the first 100 days of history. It then steeply declined during the $100 \rightarrow 1{,}000$ day time span when the slope again began to moderate. The changing compressibility-mobility term causes the instability of the b-exponent value. Note the episodic nature of the changes in the exponent value. The decline history can be divided into three production periods for this case study.

The studies of Camacho-Velazquez and Raghavan (1989) showed that the decline exponent usually does not remain constant during the life of a reservoir, and that the value of the term should become smaller over time. The wellbore pressure must increase over time if the exponent value is to remain the same.

6.2 Defining Reservoir Character

Theoretically, all production decline curves from pressure-depleting reservoirs ultimately exhibit exponential characteristics. Increasing values of b are generally caused by the addition of additional recovery mechanism to increase the effectiveness of the depletion process.

Arps (1945) and Brons (1963) were among the first investigators to recognize the values of the b-exponent term reflected reservoir character. Fetkovich (1980) and Fetkovich et al. (1987) extended these ideas to include a wider range of reservoir and depletion conditions. The following discussion categorizes reservoir and well type according to expected b value during a pressure-depletion process. However, one must be aware that there are exceptions to every rule, and the following should be treated as qualitative evaluation.

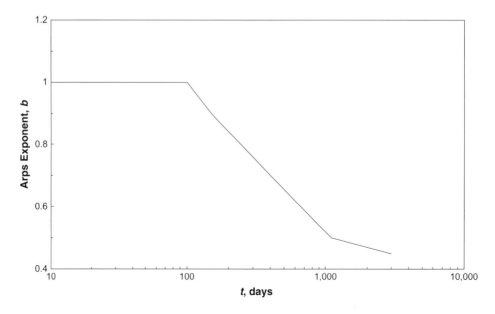

Fig. 6.4—Effect of declining pressure on b for a pressure-depleting oil reservoir (Camacho-Velazquez and Raghavan 1989).

The effect of water influx—or, in the case of oil reservoirs, gas cap expansion—is to cause an increase in the b-exponent. However, one must be aware of the consequences that the slope of the decline curve can abruptly change when breakthrough of the water or gas occurs.

6.2.1 Infinite-Acting: $b \geq 0.8$. This high value of the hyperbolic exponent is exhibited when producing from layered or naturally fractured reservoirs, with a large portion of the system producing from a very-low-permeability matrix. Usually, there is very little commingling of production at the wellbore.

6.2.2 Low-to-Moderate-GOR Oil Wells. Theoretically, the production decline for a constant-compressibility, closed reservoir with a homogeneous producing interval displays $b = 0$. This statement is true for oil reservoirs producing higher than or at the bubblepoint.

Solution-gas-drive reservoirs should generally exhibit exponent terms in the range of $0 \leq b \leq 0.8$. The lower values of $0 \leq b \leq 0.33$ are usually the product of an unfavorable mobility ratio or reservoir layering. The upper end is generally shown by rather homogeneous reservoirs producing high-API-gravity oil.

6.2.3 HGOR Oil Wells. The large and increasing gas volumes produced in conjunction with the oil generally cause the b-exponent term to be near zero.

6.2.4 Low-to-Moderate-Pressure Gas Wells. Backpressure greatly affects the slope and shape of the production decline curve and results in $0 \leq b \leq 0.5$. Typically, wells should range in the $0.4 \leq b \leq 0.5$ range but trend toward the exponential boundary with an increasing backpressure.

6.2.5 High-Pressure Gas Wells. $b = 0$ for this case because the compressibility remains essentially constant at very high pressures.

Forecasting the performance of infinite-acting reservoirs presents a problem, because production theoretically never ends. Fetkovich avoided this problem by assuming a practical drainage limit (Fetkovich 1980), while Long and Davis (1988) added an exponential decline onto the infinite-acting curve at late time.

Type curves were developed by Jacob and Lohman (1952) to study the performance of infinite-acting, homogeneous reservoirs. However, predicting production from a layered reservoir presents a difficult problem because of our inability to quantify the extent and flow capacities of the nodes within the system. There are essentially an infinite number of combinations of flow systems that may be exhibited by layered or naturally fractured reservoirs.

The type-curve analysis approach is particularly useful for analyzing the performance of reservoirs exhibiting both transient- and boundary-dominated flow conditions. Matching a type curve reflecting known boundary values onto a field production decline curve indicates that the depletion characteristics of the two should be the same. The field curve is extended outward, following the shape at the matched type curve to predict performance. The merit of applying this concept to analyze curved production histories is obvious.

Production decline-type curves are graphical representations of previously developed solutions to an equation defined by a particular set of boundary conditions. Type-curve solutions are usually presented in logarithmic and dimensionless form to cover a wide range of conditions. Equations relate the mathematical relationships between dimensionless and field conditions. A word of caution: When determining a match, the analyst assumes that the reservoir and type curves were operating under the same assumptions and boundary conditions. These assumptions and boundary conditions may not be correct. Often, the quality of the answer is predicated on the skill of the interpreter.

The first part of the following discussion applies the type-curve approach to determine reservoir permeability and predict performance for an infinite-acting reservoir.

6.3 Initializing Decline Curves

Conventional decline-curve analysis assumes a constant BHFP. However, the BHFP often changes because the production system is modified or the reservoir boundary conditions vary. A changing BHFP can cause the production decline curve to shift. Therefore, an erratic curve should be segmented into a set of smooth curves that represent periods of common characteristics.

The following discussion shows how segments of a decline curve are repositioned to a common initial time to evaluate the effect of these changing conditions on expected behavior and to analyze reservoir character.

The method of superposition divides the changing BHFP history into a series of instantaneous pressure decline steps. Application of superposition allows the constant-pressure solution to the diffusivity equation to be formed into a series expansion to calculate the cumulative effect of these changing flow rates. The time-dependent effect of the individual pressure drops on the total well-producing rate is summed to account for the flow rate during any time in the life of the reservoir. Dividing the production history into a series of producing segments represents this idea.

Example—Glenn Pool Field. The production history of the Glenn Pool field in Oklahoma discussed by Cutler (1924) is illustrated in **Fig. 6.5.** The history is divided into three producing segments. Segment 1 consists of the initial production decline curve that occurred as the field was depleted to essentially atmospheric pressure. In the second segment, the decline ceased at Year 5 when the production system was placed on vacuum and remained essentially constant to Year 9. The third segment commenced when vacuum pumping was discontinued and normal recovery methods were reinstituted. The curved semilog rate-time plot indicates the presence of either a hyperbolic or harmonic decline. What can we interpret from the production history?

The production decline history is divided into the Primary—Segment 1 and Depletion—Segment 3 periods. The Depletion period starting at Year 9 was initialized to commence at $t = 1$. The two production periods were replotted on logarithmic scales and overlaid on the Fetkovich type curve. **Fig. 6.6** illustrates the result. A match with the exponent $b = 0.4$ value was obtained, which verifies that the reservoir mechanics were the same during the primary and depletion segments of the field history.

A constant and hyperbolic exponent value should be expected because the reservoir pressure was very low. The compressibility of the system would also be expected to be high, and the relative-permeability curves would also remain essentially constant.

Example—A Kentucky Well. The producing section of a Kentucky well consists of three separate producing intervals of greatly differing permeabilities on the order of 200, 10, and 1 md. This knowledge of the field geology indicates that the decline curves should mirror a layered reservoir condition in which the decline appears harmonic. **Fig. 6.7** is the semilog rate-time plot of the well. There was a normal production decline until Month 11 (January 1986), when the well was stimulated. The effect of the stimulation treatment was to increase the producing rate from 510 to 1,800 STB/month. The EL is 134 STB/month. Note: The decline curve for the stimulation segment of the production history was gradually re-established to the approximate

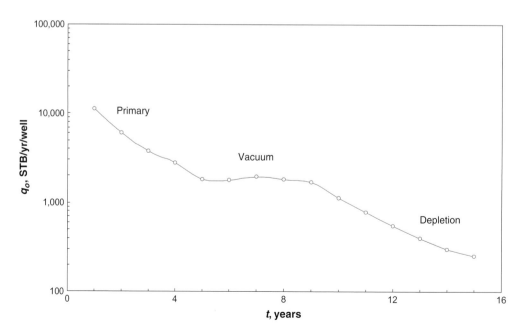

Fig. 6.5—Production history of the Glenn Pool field (Oklahoma) (Cutler 1924).

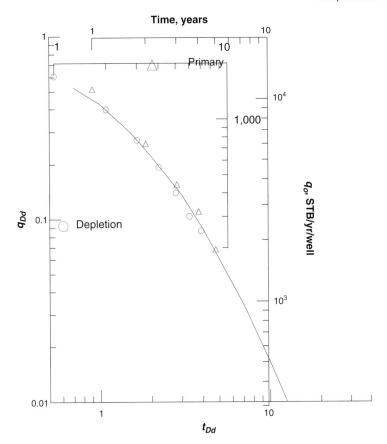

Fig. 6.6—Type-curve overlay of the Glenn Pool field.

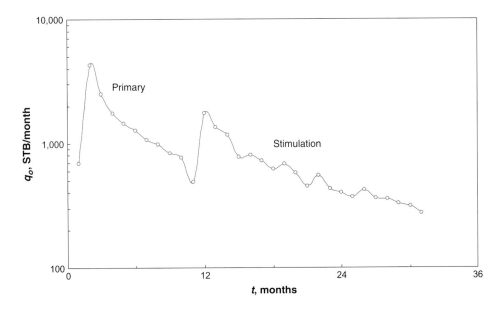

Fig. 6.7—Production history, Kentucky well. The stimulation treatment at Month 11 caused a dramatic change in the producing rate.

shape of the primary decline curve. The well history can be divided into Primary Depletion and Stimulation segments. Did the stimulation treatment materially affect ultimate recovery?

The rate-time data for the Stimulation period was initialized to start at $t = 1$ month. The data for both periods were plotted on a logarithmic scale and overlaid on the Arps-Fetkovich type curve. Dimensionless match points were selected at $t_{Dd} = 1$ and $q_{Dd} = 0.1$ on the type curve. The two field curves shown in **Fig. 6.8** are shifted, and they overlie each other.

A match with the harmonic curve was found for both the primary and stimulation cases. The harmonic match was expected, because the reservoir is layered. In actuality, an equally good fit is achieved with a $b = 0.9$ type curve. The effectiveness of the simulation treatment was estimated by comparing the expected recovery for the Primary Depletion and Stimulation production periods.

6.3.1 Production Characteristics for the Primary Segment.
Match points and the initial point coefficients are determined. The Arps (1945) harmonic equations are used to calculate the total and remaining life and reserves if the well depletes with the primary mechanism.

The match points were: $t_{Dd} = 1.0$, $t = 1.4$ months, $q_{Dd} = 0.1$, and $q = 540$ STB/month.

The last production rate read from the curve, $q = 730$ STB/month.

Apply rearranged forms of the Fetkovich relationships, Eqs. 1.31 and 1.32.

$$q_i = \frac{q_2}{q_{Dd}} = \frac{540 \text{ STB/month}}{0.1} = 5,400 \text{ STB/month}$$

$$D_i = \frac{t_{Dd}}{t} = \frac{1}{1.4 \text{ months}} = 0.714/\text{month}$$

Total and remaining life. The EL is 134 STB/month; the initial potential (IP) is 5,400 STB/month. Applying Eq. 1.26,

$$\text{Total life: IP} \to \text{EL}: t = \frac{q_i - q}{D_i q} = \frac{(5,400 - 134)\text{STB/month}}{(0.714/\text{month})(134 \text{ STB/month})} = 55 \text{ months}$$

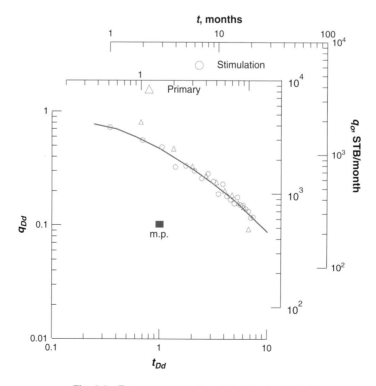

Fig. 6.8—Type-curve overlay of the Kentucky field.

Remaining life: IP $\rightarrow$ 1/86: $t = \dfrac{q_i - q}{D_i q} = \dfrac{(5,400 - 730)\text{STB/month}}{(0.714/\text{month})(730\ \text{STB/month})} = 9$ months

Ultimate recovery and reserves.
Applying Eq. 1.28,

Total reserves: IP $\rightarrow$ EL: $N_p = \dfrac{q_i}{D_i}\ln\dfrac{q_i}{q_2} = \dfrac{5,400\ \text{STB/month}}{0.714/\text{month}}\ln\left(\dfrac{5,400}{134}\right) = 27{,}955$ STB

Reserves: IP $\rightarrow$ 1/86: $N_p = \dfrac{5,400\ \text{STB/month}}{0.714/\text{month}}\ln\left(\dfrac{5,400}{730}\right) = 15{,}134$ STB

The oil remaining to be produced at the time of the stimulation treatment in January 1986:
Primary depletion reserves remaining at 1/86 = 27,955 – 15,134 = 12,821 STB.

6.3.2 Production Characteristics After the Stimulation Treatment. Match points and the initial point coefficients are determined. The Arps (1945) harmonic equations are used to calculate the production characteristics because the match indicated $b = 1$.
   Match points: $t_{Dd} = 1$, $t = 2.9$ months, $q_{Dd} = 0.1$, and $q = 250$ STB/month.
   The last production rate read from the curve, $q = 730$ STB/month.

$q_i = \dfrac{q_2}{q_{Dd}} = \dfrac{250\ \text{STB/month}}{0.1} = 2{,}500$ STB/month

$D_i = \dfrac{t_{Dd}}{q_{Dd}} = \dfrac{1}{2.9\ \text{months}} = 0.345/\text{month}$

The total and remaining life. The EL is 134 STB/month.

Total life: IP $\rightarrow$ EL: $t = \dfrac{q_i - q}{D_i q} = \dfrac{(2,500 - 134)\text{STB/month}}{(0.345/\text{month})(134\ \text{STB/month})} = 51$ months

Remaining life: IP $\rightarrow$ 1/86: $t = \dfrac{q_i - q}{D_i q} = \dfrac{(2,500 - 280)\text{STB/month}}{(0.345/\text{month})(280\ \text{STB/month})} = 23$ months

Ultimate recovery and reserves.
Applying Eq. 1.28,

Ultimate recovery: IP $\rightarrow$ EL: $N_p = \dfrac{q_i}{D_i}\ln\dfrac{q_i}{q_2} = \dfrac{2,500\ \text{STB/month}}{0.345/\text{month}}\ln\left(\dfrac{2,500}{134}\right) = 21{,}204$ STB

Reserves: IP $\rightarrow$ 1/86: $N_p = \dfrac{2,500\ \text{STB/month}}{0.345/\text{month}}\ln\left(\dfrac{2,500}{280}\right) = 15{,}864$ STB

Reserves = 21,204 to 15,864 = 5,340 STB

   The calculation indicated 12,821 STB remained to be produced under the Primary Depletion case. Recovery was increased to a 21,204 STB by the stimulation treatment. Therefore, the stimulation treatment recovered 8,383 STB of additional oil. The stimulation treatment therefore increased the ultimate recovery.

6.4 When $b > 1$

The Arps (1945) exponential and hyperbolic rate-time relationships are based on the assumption that production ultimately declines to zero. Otherwise, the expected production for decline curves displaying b values greater than 1 theoretically extends to infinite time. Particularly within the United States, there are any number of producing areas where a good fit of the well-performance history can be achieved for such b values when the generalized rate-time relationship (Eq. 1.9) is used as the curve-fitting equation. Performance histories of highly-variable-permeability, layered, and naturally fractured reservoirs often exhibit this phenomenon. These large exponent values are the product of long-lived crossflow caused by oil or gas feeding from very-low-permeability to high-permeability zones, which in turn act as conduits to the wellbore.

Arps (1945), and more recently Kelkar and Perez (1988), felt that conventional decline analysis techniques were not applicable for studying this type of flow condition. The inability of the $b \geq 1$ values to converge to zero nullifies their application by the usual Arps decline-curve analysis methods. Fetkovich (1980) stated that $b > 1$ decline curves reflect transient conditions and should not be applied to the Arps (1945) solution techniques. He developed a set of transient type curves that ultimately trend to boundary-dominated flow conditions (Fetkovich 1980). The correlation coefficient used is the relationship of the wellbore radius to the outer-boundary limit. Production is forecast out to some reasonable time limit or to an assumed drainage area. The Fetkovich method combines his theoretically correct type-curve approach with reasonable assumptions of reservoir character to solve the problem.

Long and Davis (1988) divided the decline curve into transient- and boundary-dominated segments. A type curve provides the basis for extrapolating the field data into the future for the transient portion of the performance forecast. An exponential decline is added at late time to force the transient curve to converge to an endpoint within some realistic time frame. The time of onset and decline rate of the exponential curve are determined from knowledge of the field characteristics. **Fig. 6.9** illustrates the concept of marrying an infinite-acting, transient curve to a late-time exponential decline. Appending the exponential curve onto the flat-lying portion of the transient curve forces the well to cease production at 18 years for this particular illustration. The Long and Davis idea lacks theoretical foundation but is a reasonable attempt to solve a widespread problem.

Preselected $q_i = 10,000$ units/month and $D_i = 100\%$/month coefficients and varying b values were input by Long and Davis (1988) into the rate-time relationship (Eq. 1.9) to develop type curves for the transient portion of the solution method. Matching the field curve to the type-curve match when both curves are plotted on the same scale determines the "most likely" b-exponent value. The match reflects the exponent coefficient defining the characteristics of the performance data.

A second figure expresses each hyperbolic curve as a series of incremental, continuous decline-rate values. Onset of the exponential decline begins at the time when the exponential decline is the same as the

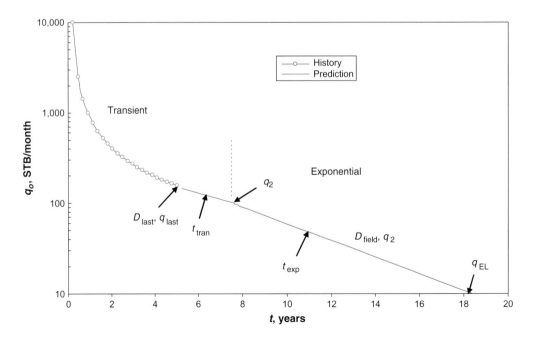

Fig. 6.9—Appending the exponential ending to the transient decline curve. A curve fit with the general rate-time equation provides the transient side, while the exponential side is derived from field decline characteristics.

predetermined field decline value. The exponential decline continues until the well goes off production at the EL. On the surface, the assumption of a late-time exponential decline appears to be unwarranted. However, one generally develops a "feel" for the average characteristics of wells producing in a particular geological and geographical region. Initial producing and decline rates and the exponent value are usually reflected by early- to mid-time production characteristics, while late-time performance is a function of the more flat-lying rate-time curve as it slowly declines toward the EL.

Inclusion of both loss ratio and instantaneous exponential decline equations in the Long and Davis (1988) analysis method caused the calculation procedure to be somewhat complicated. The following discussion applies the definition of the continuous decline rate to develop a more straightforward, although not a more technically correct, approach.

6.4.1 Development of Equations. The general hyperbolic rate-time relationship shown in Eq. 1.9 provides the starting point for the construction of the transient type curves. As previously stated, the input parameters used to generate the Long and Davis (1988) type curves were $q_i = 10,000$ units/month and $D_i = 100\%$/month. The 100%/month decline rate is equivalent to a 1,200%/year decline rate. **Fig. 6.10** presents an amended set of the Long and Davis type curves generated from Eq. 1.9 for a 20-year time period. A harmonic decline curve was included in the figure for completeness. Exponent values b range from 0 to 2. The exponential curve is essentially vertical on this particular scale.

Incremental continuous exponential decline rates trending along each of the b-exponent stems were calculated with Eq. 1.12. **Fig. 6.11** represents the progression of these changing exponential decline rates with increasing time for each exponent stem. Decline rates lying outside the 5% / year $\leq D \leq$ 50% / year ranges were excluded from the figure to emphasize the region of interest.

The initial decline rate of 1,200%/year selected by Long and Davis (1988) as the starting point was probably chosen to maximize the spread of the type curves. **Fig. 6.12** compares the spread of the boundary curves for two different initial decline rates. The spread of the boundaries for the $D_i = 1,200\%$/year solution is much greater than the $D_i = 80\%$/year solution.

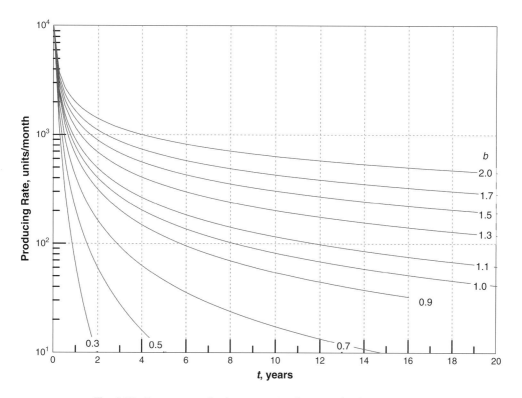

Fig. 6.10—Type curves for b-exponent values varying between 0 and 2.

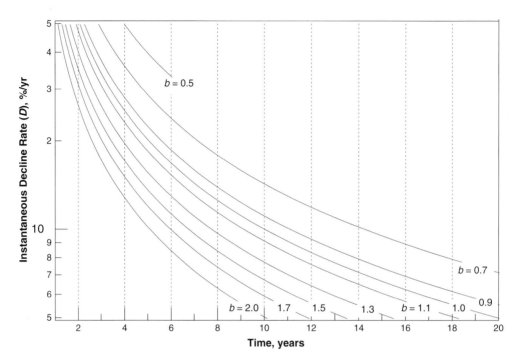

Fig. 6.11—Yearly decline rates calculated from Fig. 6.10.

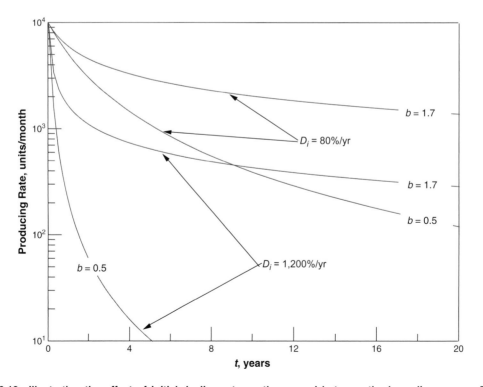

Fig. 6.12—Illustrating the effect of initial decline rate on the spread between the bounding curves. The figure indicates that the initial decline rate profoundly changes the shape of the $b = 0.5$ curve.

The shapes of the $b = 1.7$ curves for either the D_i of 80% and 1,200% stems are approximately the same in Fig. 6.12. This fact illustrates one of the fundamental characteristics of this approximation technique. Type curves reflecting different initial rate and decline rate values can produce an equally good match of the field performance curve at middle to late time. Therefore, an equally good fit can be achieved with more than one combination of the D_i, q_i, and b coefficients. Selection of any particular combination of coefficients does not necessarily mean it is "the best" fit.

6.4.2 Analysis Procedure. The total prediction period illustrated in Fig. 6.9 covers the remaining transient and imposed exponential decline time segments. The following expression presents the summation equation:

$$\text{Prediction Period} = t_{\text{trans}} + t_{\text{exp}}. \quad\quad\quad\quad\quad\quad\quad\quad\quad\quad (6.6)$$

Generate a semilog rate-time plot of the field data on the same scale as the type curve to begin the analysis process. Overlay the field curve on the type curve, and obtain a match. Determine the exponent value b for the transient portion of the history. The prediction is now divided into the remaining transient and exponential segments.

Define the onset of the exponential decline. The onset of the exponential curve is defined as the time when the interval exponential decline rate on the transient curve is the same as the assumed field decline rate D_{field}. Read along the selected b stem in the decline rate-time plot, shown as Fig. 6.11, to the point at which the stem and stipulated field decline rates are the same. This point defines the onset of the exponential portion of the prediction.

The time difference t_{trans} between the start of the exponential decline and the last recorded data point q_{last} represents the transient conditions portion of the prediction. The exponential decline period t_{exp} spans the time between the start of the exponential decline and the end at the EL. Refer to Fig. 6.9 for reference to the different line segments.

Evaluate the transient portion of the curve. Rewrite the hyperbolic rate-time Eq. 1.9 to reflect the selection of any point on curve as the initial or starting point defined as q_{last}. The equation is only applicable to the transient portion of the prediction.

$$q_2 = \frac{q_{\text{last}}}{\left(1 + bD_{\text{last}}t\right)^{1/b}}. \quad\quad\quad\quad\quad\quad\quad\quad\quad\quad (6.7)$$

The three coefficients defining a particular field curve are the b-exponent interpreted from the match to the type curve; the preselected field decline rate, D_{last}, interpreted from the decline history match with Fig. 6.11; and the last historical rate on the transient curve, q_{last}, interpreted from the match of the type curve.

The producing rate at the onset of the exponential decline and any rates occurring during transient conditions can be read along the type curve or calculated with Eq. 6.7. Calculate cumulative production with an amended version of Eq. 1.22.

$$Q_p = \frac{q_{\text{last}}}{D_{\text{last}}\left(1 - b\right)}\left[1 - \left(\frac{q_2}{q_{\text{last}}}\right)^{1-b}\right]. \quad\quad\quad\quad\quad\quad\quad\quad\quad\quad (6.8)$$

Evaluate the exponential portion of the curve. The rate at the onset of the exponential decline was previously determined from the type-curve match. The time interval spanning the period between the onset of the exponential decline and the EL is calculated with Eq. 1.13, while cumulative production is calculated with Eq. 1.16. Both equations are amended to reflect the characteristics of this prediction method.

$$t = \frac{\ln\left(\dfrac{q_2}{q_{\text{EL}}}\right)}{D_{\text{field}}}. \quad\quad\quad\quad\quad\quad\quad\quad\quad\quad (6.9)$$

$$Q_p = \frac{q_2 - q_{\text{EL}}}{D_{\text{field}}}. \quad\quad\quad\quad\quad\quad\quad\quad\quad\quad (6.10)$$

Develop the expected history of the exponential portion of the performance prediction by plotting and connecting the two rate-time end points on the field curve. Future rates are read from the straight line or calculated with a modified form of Eq. 1.8.

$$q = q_2 \exp\left(-D_{\text{field}}t\right). \quad \dots\dots\dots\dots\dots\dots\dots\dots\dots\dots\dots\dots\dots\dots\dots\dots\dots\dots\dots \quad (6.11)$$

Cumulate the transient and exponential histories. Total cumulative production is the sum of the production credited during the transient and exponential periods.

Example. An analysis of a Spraberry well from the Arlick (west Texas) lease illustrates the analysis procedure. The EL of the well is 100 STB/month. Reservoir and production analysis experience in the Spraberry trend has shown a late time 5% exponential decline rate is common (i.e., $D_{\text{field}} = 5\%$). Predict the remaining well performance history.

Match the field and type curve to determine coefficients of the transient hyperbola. **Fig. 6.13** indicates a match with the $b = 1.7$ curve.

The last data point read from the smoothed curve is $q_{\text{last}} = 175$ STB/month at 9.4 years. Transient-producing rates can be interpolated along the hyperbolic stem to predict future performance until the onset of the exponential decline.

Determine the time of onset of the exponential curve. Examination of Fig. 6.11 indicates that a 5%/yr decline occurs at 12 years on the $b = 1.7$ stem. An exponential decline is assumed to begin after this point. Read $D_{\text{last}} = 6.3\%$/yr decline rate from the same figure at 9.4 years.

Define the transient portion of the prediction. These initial efforts determined the coefficients for the decline-curve equation for the transient side are: $b = 1.7$, D_{last} at 9.4 years = 6.3%/yr, q_{last} at 9.4 years = 175 STB/month, and $t_{\text{trans}} = 12.0 - 9.4 = 2.6$ years.

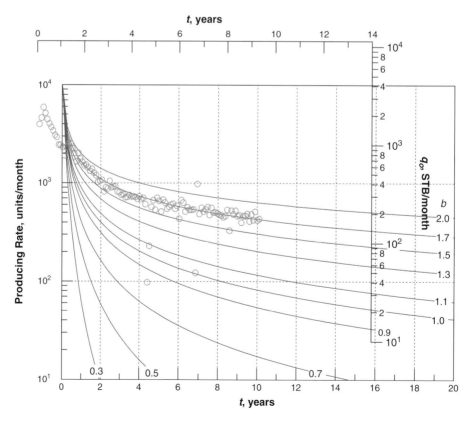

Fig. 6.13—Type-curve match with Arlick lease production history. Transferring information to Fig. 6.11 indicates that the 5%/yr rate begins at 12 years.

The coefficients are input into the rate-time Eq. 6.7 to form an equation describing the transient portion of the decline curve extending beyond the last historical data point out to the start of the exponential curve.

$$q_2 = \frac{q_{last}}{\left(1 + bD_{last}t\right)^{1/b}}$$

$$q_2 = \frac{q_{last}}{\left(1 + bD_{last}t\right)^{1/b}} = \frac{175 \text{ STB/month}}{\left[1 + (1.7)(0.063)(t - 9.4)\right]^{1/1.7}} = \frac{175 \text{ STB/month}}{\left[1 + (0.11)(t - 9.4)\right]^{1/1.7}}$$

The producing rate at 12 years can be obtained by inspection or by applying the previous equation:

$$q_2 = \frac{175 \text{ STB/month}}{\left[1 + (0.11)(12 - 9.4)\right]^{0.59}} = 153 \text{ STB/month}$$

Cumulative production during the transient period. Apply Eq. 6.8.

$$N_p = \frac{q_{last}}{D_{last}(1 - b)}\left[1 - \left(\frac{q_2}{q_{last}}\right)^{1-b}\right] = \frac{(12 \text{ months/yr})(175)}{(0.063/\text{yr})(1 - 1.7)}\left[1 - \left(\frac{153}{175}\right)^{1-1.7}\right] = 4,696 \text{ STB}$$

Define the extent of the exponential curve. Examination of Fig. 6.11 indicates that a 5% decline occurs at 12 years on the $b = 1.7$ curve. The exponential decline begins after this point. Read the rate value at 12 years directly from the match shown in Fig. 6.13, or use Eq. 6.7 to calculate the value.

Cumulative production during the exponential period. The EL is 100 STB/month. Apply Eq. 6.10.

$$N_p = \frac{q_2 - q_{EL}}{D_{field}} = \frac{(153 - 100)12 \text{ months/yr}}{0.05} = 12,720 \text{ STB}.$$

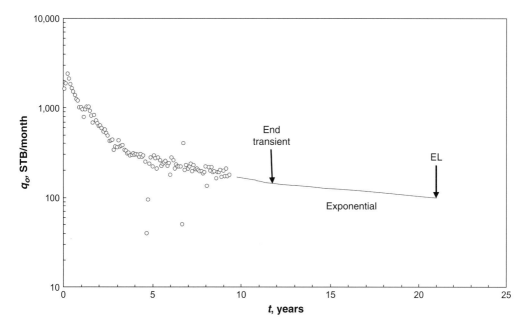

Fig. 6.14—Historical and predicted performance for the Arlick lease.

Length of exponential period. Apply Eq. 6.9.

$$t = \frac{\ln\left(\dfrac{q_2}{q_{EL}}\right)}{D_{field}} = \frac{\ln\left(\dfrac{153}{100}\right)}{0.05} = 8.5 \text{ years.}$$

Total expected production: $4{,}696 + 12{,}720 = 17{,}416$ STB.

Cumulative future production for the Arlick lease well was determined to be 17,416 STB. The expected future yearly rate values were calculated and are shown in **Fig. 6.14.** The calculation indicates that the well should produce under transient conditions for an additional 2.6 years. After that, production declines at a predetermined 5%/yr rate at the onset of exponential conditions and then attains the EL 8.5 years later.

In reality, an equally good match of the transient portion of the curve can be achieved with $0.8 \le b \le 1.7$ exponent terms. We should include all known information about the reservoir system and have an idea of the exponent from the reservoir mechanics when this type of analysis is performed, which guides us in the best fit to use.

Chapter 7

Production Performance Plots

Declining production may be caused not only by a loss of reservoir pressure but also by increasing volumes of secondary fluid(s) entering the wellstream. Secondary fluids in the case of an oil well are gas and water, while water is the secondary fluid for a gas well.

Water production is usually the result of early-time water breakthrough to the well from the more permeable zones in a layered reservoir or upward cusping from an underlying aquifer (i.e., a bottomwaterdrive reservoir). The water production rate is a function of the strength of the waterdrive, characteristics of reservoir fluids, and vertical and horizontal permeability distribution of the reservoir rock. Liberated solution or gas-cap gas commingled in the producing stream takes up a proportionate volume in the producing string and therefore reduces the oil rate. In any case, there is a decrease in the primary fluid volumes. The Arps (1945) concepts and decline-curve analysis methods apply only to the first category of declining production. This chapter develops methods for analyzing the declining production performance of a reservoir because of secondary-fluid production through the use of fluid ratio performance plots.

Water-disposal costs may be excessive for low-rate oil or gas wells. Produced water must be transported to a disposal well for injection into a designated sand, cleaned and used in a waterflood, or dumped into an evaporation pond. In these cases, estimating operating expenses can be as important as predicting future sales volumes, because disposal costs can approach income. Production performance or fluid ratio data are plotted to analyze the changing relations of primary- to secondary-fluid production volumes. The following discussion shows that these changing fluid volumes are directly related to relative-permeability concepts and illustrates the more common types of fluid ratio plots.

The first part of the discussion develops the conventional producing ratio-cumulative recovery plots for both homogeneous and layered reservoirs. These figures are readily constructed and easily converted to comparing expected income to operating costs. The latter half of the chapter develops prediction techniques founded on relative-permeability and frontal-advance concepts to monitor the efficiency of the recovery process. These methods provide an additional aid for characterizing the reservoir.

7.1 Fluid Ratio Plots

Performance data plots involve GOR, WOR, gas/water ratio (GWR), or gas/liquid ratio (GLR) as well as pressure values. Examples of these plotting methods were discussed in Chapter 2. Remember, the simultaneous analysis of rate-time and production-performance plots greatly increases the quality of any prediction.

7.1.1 Fundamental Relationships. Oil, gas, or water effective permeability (k_o, k_g, or k_w) is a measure of the ability of a porous material to allow transmission of a specific fluid. Relative-permeability curves are ratio curves showing the changing relationship between two fluids flowing simultaneously through the same system. **Fig. 7.1** presents the effect of increasing water saturation on a semilog water-to-oil relative-permeability (k_w/k_o) curve. The inverse k_o/k_w curve is included for later reference. The k_w/k_o curve changes as a function of increasing water saturation, while the k_o/k_w curve is the inverse. Changes in water saturation at low to moderate values cause measured increases in the ability of the system to flow water. However, at increased water-saturation values, small saturation changes can profoundly increase the ability of the system to transmit water

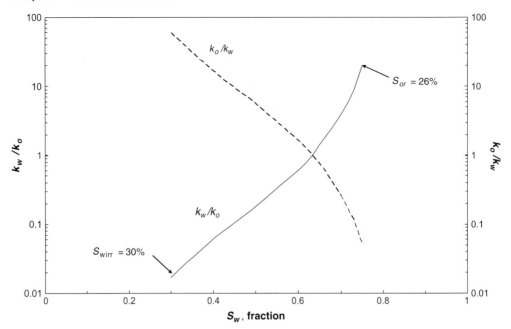

Fig. 7.1—Example water/oil relative-permeability curve for a water-displacing-oil system. Note: Water and oil flow only over the S_{wirr} = 30% to S_{or} = 26% range.

in preference to oil production. Note: The first and last part of each curve can be represented by two reasonable straightline approximations. More information about this type of curve is discussed later in the chapter.

Water does not begin flowing in the system until the water saturation increases to at least the S_{wirr} = 30% value in Fig. 7.1. For most cases, this threshold is equivalent to the initial water saturation, S_{wi}. Conversely, water continually displaces oil until achieving the residual oil saturation S_{or} = 26% threshold. At this point, the remaining oil is immovable, unless some type of enhanced recovery process is instituted to change the fluid or reservoir flow system character.

Relative-permeability ratios can be calculated from field production data or by special core analysis tests. Core analysis studies measure the characteristics of a single, essentially homogeneous rock plug, while performance data include the changing effects of field operations and reservoir character as well as the average relative permeability displayed by the producing interval. Either method has its good and bad points.

Produced fluid ratio plots reflect the changing flow rates of fluids in a two- or three-phase system. Couple this observation with Darcy's law to derive Eq. 7.1 for an oil/water flow system. The equation indicates that the WOR is a function of the oil and water viscosities, effective permeabilities, and formation volume factors. By inspection of the equation, a high-viscosity oil can be seen and should display a considerably greater WOR than a more moderate viscosity oil because water viscosity is usually on the order of 1 cp.

$$\text{WOR} = \frac{q_w}{q_o} = \frac{B_o}{B_w} \frac{\mu_o}{\mu_w} \frac{k_w}{k_o} . \quad\dots\dots\dots\dots\dots\dots\dots\dots\dots\dots\dots\dots\dots\dots\dots\dots \quad (7.1)$$

The same concept can be expressed for the case for an oil reservoir operating below the bubble point when oil and gas are flowing simultaneously. However, in this case, the producing GOR is the sum of the gas volume dissolved in the reservoir oil (i.e., solution gas) and free gas flowing in the reservoir.

$$\text{GOR} = \frac{q_g}{q_o} = R_s + \frac{B_o}{B_g} \frac{\mu_o}{\mu_g} \frac{k_g}{k_o} . \quad\dots\dots\dots\dots\dots\dots\dots\dots\dots\dots\dots\dots\dots\dots\dots\dots \quad (7.2)$$

Eq. 7.3 defines the fractional flow term, f_w, in the context of the water and oil volumes flowing in a reservoir. Note: The f_w is also related to the WOR. Gas/oil or gas/water relationships can be derived in a similar manner.

$$f_w = \frac{q_w}{q_t} = \frac{q_w}{q_w + q_o} = \frac{\text{WOR}}{\text{WOR} + 1} . \quad\dots\dots\dots\dots\dots\dots\dots\dots\dots\dots\dots\dots\dots\dots \quad (7.3)$$

Applying the previous equations to analyze field production data can provide insight into reservoir character. However, the smooth curve in Fig. 7.1 was developed for a homogeneous rock section. One is seldom so fortunate to be presented with an opportunity to produce from a constant rock property interval. Usually, the productive section is composed of a series of rock layers of differing permeabilities, rock properties, and crossflow capabilities. This variation either can be of only minor consequence or exhibit profoundly heterogeneous characteristics, which in this case would cause a water-displacing-oil process to occur in a layered system.

Nind (1981) discusses the case of water encroaching and differentially displacing oil in a layered reservoir. Water coursing more easily through the highest-permeability layers causes breakthrough to a producing well to occur in these layers. Therefore, a field WOR curve can exhibit a series of steplike WOR increases as a function of water breakthrough from decreasing-permeability layers.

Fig. 7.2 is an idealized case showing the effect of water breakthrough on the WOR-N_p curve for a two-layer system.

The WOR abruptly changes after breakthrough of Layer 1 because of the increasing ability of water to flow through the highest-transmissibility sand. Most of the movable oil has been displaced, and water becomes the predominant fluid flowing. A similar sequence starts when water breakthrough occurs in the second-most-permeable layer. The WOR again dramatically increases when the water breaks through to the producing well in Layer 2.

The effect of reservoir layering and changing operating conditions on the shape of a field plot are developed in the next section. The discussion is written in the context of oil/water relationships. However, the same procedures can be used for studying oil-gas and gas-water relationships.

7.1.2 The WOR Plot. **Fig. 7.3** illustrates an idealized case for rectangular and semilog WOR vs. N_p plots of the production history for a water-displacing-oil system from a homogeneous sand.

The curvature of the rectangular plot at early time is quite pronounced. However, the curve flattens with increased production as water becomes the predominantly produced fluid. The semilog plot representing the same system is a straight line. Therefore, the logarithm of WOR can be assumed to be linearly proportional to cumulative recovery. This observation coincides with the Buckley-Leverett theory describing a straightline

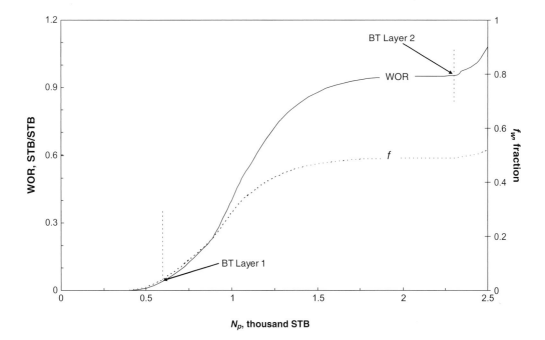

Fig. 7.2—The WOR and f_w behavior of a well producing from an idealized two-layered, waterdrive reservoir. Note: The fraction of water flowing in the reservoir is approximately 50%, while WOR = 0.6 STB/STB. The WOR curve appears to be more expressive than the f_w curve.

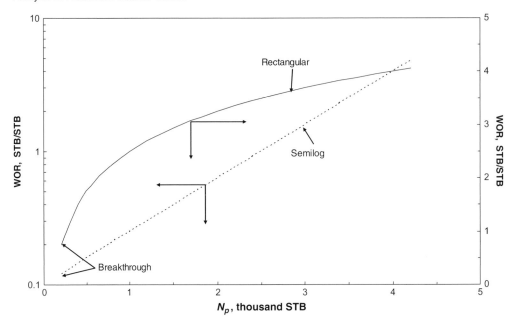

Fig. 7.3—An idealized WOR vs. N_p plot on rectangular and semilog coordinates of a well producing from a homogeneous interval. Note the straightline relationship of the semilog curve. Performance prediction for the semilog case would be quite straightforward, while it would be somewhat problematical for the rectangular case because of the arcuate nature of the curve.

relationship when the logarithm of WOR is plotted vs. cumulative recovery for a water-displacing-oil, linear homogeneous system (Buckley and Leverett 1942).

The effects of waterflooding heterogeneous reservoirs are often monitored by replacing the cumulative-recovery term on the x axis with cumulative-water injection values (i.e., W_i). Application of either method produces curves of equal character. The expected straightline relationship is easily extrapolated into the future. However, the logarithmic scale compresses the WOR values. Exact oil-to-water volume relationships may be difficult to interpret with the compressed scale when a producing property is operating close to its EL, and disposal costs are the primary factor for determining if the property is to be allowed to remain on production. An alternate and better plotting method in this case is to use the OWR vs. cumulative-production plot.

7.1.3 The OWR Plot. Sometimes, a better method to predict water-handling costs is a semilog plot of OWR vs. cumulative recovery. This plotting method permits a more precise estimate of barrels of oil produced in relation to the volume of water produced because the curve is trending to an ever-expanding scale. OWR plots tend to emphasize the latter part of the production history, which is usually the region of most interest. **Fig. 7.4** is an illustration for homogeneous sand producing under constant field conditions when the straightline characteristic is assumed to be present over the N_{p1} and N_{p2} cumulative-production time span.

7.2 Factors Affecting the Shape of the Curve
The previous discussion showed that multiple sand layers within a producing section often cause water production to increase in a stepwise manner. A pronounced increase of water production occurs when the waterfront in each layer sequentially breaks through. The field relative-permeability curve for the multizone producing interval may appear stepped because it is a function of the composite flow characteristics of all of the layers and has been shown to be related to the producing WOR.

Prats et al. (1959) applied basic equations and concepts to compare waterflood behavior in an idealized, layered model. **Fig. 7.5** presents the history for the simulated waterflood of the four-layer system. The effective conductivity, kh, for each of the four layers varied from 1,472 md-ft for the highest-permeability Layer 1 to 366 md-ft for the lowest-permeability Layer 4. The stair-step WOR curve represents the time of breakthrough for each sand, which occurred initially in the highest-permeability sand. The flat portion and

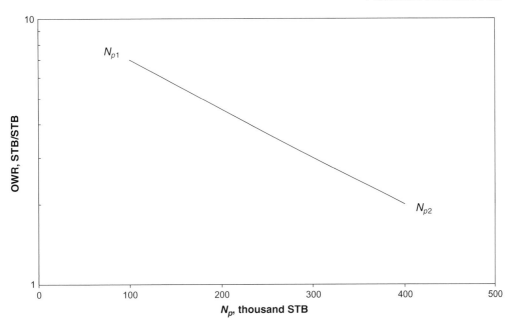

Fig. 7.4—An idealized semilog OWR-N_p plot. Theoretically, the logarithm of the OWR should be a straight line because cumulative production increases from N_{p1} to N_{p2}.

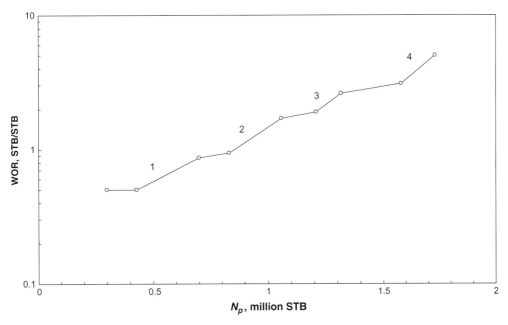

Fig. 7.5—WOR history in a layered reservoir reflects a series of stepwise WOR increases as the more permeable zones sequentially water out (Prats et al. 1959).

increasing WOR of Period 1 represents a composite of the field relative-permeability characteristics of all four layers, while the flat and increasing WOR of Period 2 represents a composite of the permeability to oil comprising the second through the fourth layers. At this time, mainly water is flowing through Layer 1. Water production increases immediately after breakthrough. This illustration is equivalent to four Fig. 7.2 figures superimposed upward in order of decreasing sand permeability. Again, we see the inherent relationship between the WOR and the k_o/k_w curve.

Changes in field operations may also affect the shape of the plot. Field operations can involve changes in injected-water volumes, well-pumping efficiency, well downtime, or infield well pattern.

7.2.1 Layering and Changes in Operations Examples. The production history of a simultaneous water-flood of the Cypress and Benoist sands located in a 700-acre unit of the Illinois basin is shown in **Fig. 7.6** (Timmerman 1971). Two straightline approximations of the performance curve are apparent. The first straight line represents Period 1 and reflects the combined production from both the sands. The second straight line, representing Period 2, occurs after the higher-permeability Benoist sand flooded out, and the lower-permeability Cypress sand provides the majority of the produced oil. The increased slope of the line indicates that the efficiency of the water-displacing-oil process has declined, because more water is produced for each barrel of produced oil. Oil production peaked at the time of the intersection of the two straight lines. The reduced volume of produced water starting at the 9-million-STB cumulative-production period is the result of shutting in high-WOR wells. However, the last two data points may indicate the possibility of a return to the Period 2 decline characteristics.

Individual well history differences are included in a fieldwide composite curve. This field curve is a combination of the reservoir rock and fluid character as well as operational characteristics. The expanding scale of the OWR curve more accurately defines the future oil rate of high water cut.

Example. The previously discussed ideas were used to study the performance history of a multilayered oil reservoir waterflooded for a number of years (City of Long Beach 1964; Lijek 1989). **Fig. 7.7** presents a semilog plot of the performance history of the field.

Field development occurred during Years 1 and 2. Water injection started in Year 3. The maximum oil production rate peaked in approximately Year 3 at 13,600 STB/D. Exponential declines are apparent over the year 11 → 16 and 18 → 24 intervals. Other, subsidiary straightline approximations are also apparent. No conclusions can be drawn from these observations other than that portions of the semilog rate-time plot are exponential in nature.

The increasing WOR curve is the result of the cycling of injected water. Depletion and watering out of the major pay sands and continued water cycling caused the oil production rate to decline to approximately 3,000 STB/D. Water injection rates varied from 20,000 to 40,000 STB/D. There has been little change in the GOR since the waterflood was initiated. The number of wells on production stayed essentially the same after Year 4 even though there was a dramatic increase of the WOR.

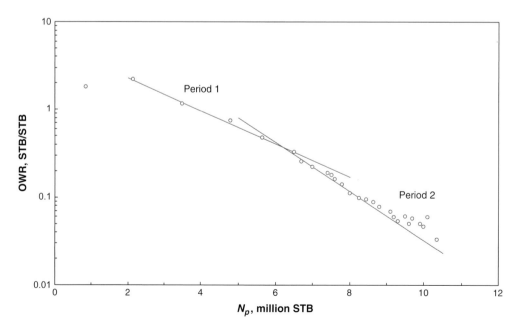

Fig. 7.6—Commingled example (Timmerman 1971). Oil production during Period 1 is from the Benoist and Cypress sands, while Period 2 production is principally derived from the lower-permeability Cypress sand after floodout of the Benoist sand. The increased slope with time indicates that more water must be processed to produce a barrel of oil.

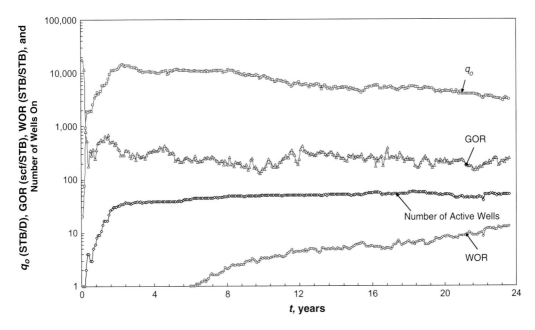

Fig. 7.7—Performance history: example field (City of Long Beach 1964). The continual increase in WOR is caused by the increasing inefficiencies of the displacement process.

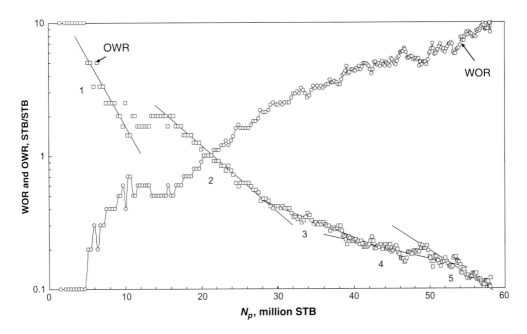

Fig. 7.8—Semilog OWR and WOR plots: example field (City of Long Beach 1964). Straightline approximations divide the performance history into five segments or periods. The line slope during Period 5 appears to represent a time when water production was dramatically increasing.

Fig. 7.8 is a semilog plot of the OWR and the inverse WOR-producing histories. It is obvious that better-quality straightline approximations of the performance history can be made on the expanded scale of the OWR curve. The performance history is divided into five periods, each with distinctive water/oil-producing characteristics. These straight lines describe a constancy of depletion conditions. The decreasing slope of the OWR curve reflects the reduced ability of the field to produce oil, because the highest-transmissibility sands

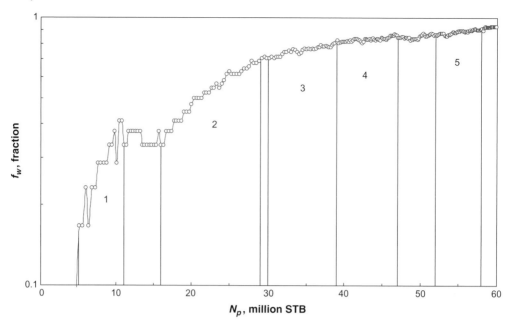

Fig. 7.9—Fraction of water flowing as a function of cumulative production: example field. Note the inclination of the f_w curve during Period 5.

are the first to suffer breakthrough, water out, and become depleted. Each of these straight lines is equivalent to the field relative-permeability curve operating in the reservoir during that particular production interval. Note: These straightline approximations encompass most of the reservoir-production history. Field production data were included with Eq. 7.3 to calculate the fractional flow curve shown in **Fig. 7.9.**

Oil is displaced in a piston-like manner early in the life of the waterflood. Breakthrough of injected water to some of the offsetting producing wells caused the fraction of water flowing in the reservoir to begin to dramatically increase after 17 million STB was produced. The curve assumes a hyperbolic shape. Another phase in the depletion history of the unit begins at the 52-million-STB cumulative-production level. The increased slope diverging from the smooth curve indicates that the displacement process has become less efficient. More than 90% of the fluids flowing into the reservoir were water at the end of the history.

7.3 The "X" Plot Method

Ershaghi and Omorigie (1978) and Ershaghi and Abdassah (1984) combined the fractional flow equation and Buckley-Leverett displacement concepts to develop a method for predicting performance and determining the field relative-permeability ratio curve.

Three major assumptions form the basis for this method. Recognizing the strengths and weaknesses of these assumptions provides a foundation to the understanding of the "X" plot method. These assumptions are as follows:

- A linear and homogeneous system. Ershaghi and Abdassah (1984) showed that the concept is also applicable to other reservoir shapes. This assumption does not necessarily relegate this technique to a lesser status, because all simplified performance analysis methods require the reservoir to be fitted to a specific geometric outline.
- A k_o/k_w vs. N_p plot can be represented by straightline approximations and is a composite of the characteristics of the entire producing interval.

Ershaghi and Abdassah (1984) stated that the X plot method is valid only for $f_w > 0.5$ values because the relative-permeability ratio curve is relatively straight only at high-water saturations (Ershaghi and Abdassah

1984). Lo et al. (1990) developed a theory and used simulation studies to show that the semilog WOR vs. N_p plot produces a straight line at earlier times than the X plot method.

Constant operating conditions are assumed. This assumption is not inherently bad because the previously discussed methods, as well as most simplified prediction methods, assume constant operating conditions.

7.3.1 Fundamental Relationships. The following development combines the semilog k_o/k_w vs. S_w straightline assumption with frontal-advance theory. Welge defined the fraction of water flowing in terms of the effects of relative permeability and viscosity ratio in an oil/water system when gravity is neglected (Welge 1952).

$$f_w = \frac{1}{1 + \dfrac{k_o}{k_w}\dfrac{\mu_w}{\mu_o}}. \quad \dots\dots\dots\dots\dots\dots\dots\dots\dots\dots\dots\dots\dots\dots\dots \quad (7.4)$$

The Straightline Approximation. Ershaghi and Omorigie (1978) assumed that a straight line is a good approximation during the late-time portion of the k_o/k_w curve. Therefore, apply the equation of a straight line with a negative slope to the semilog relative-permeability ratio vs. S_w plot. In a practical sense, cumulative-oil production N_p may be substituted for the water-saturation term because any increase in water saturation in the system can result only by producing a corresponding oil volume. Therefore, replace the S_w term with the cumulative-oil production term N_p to form Eq. 7.5.

$$\ln\frac{k_o}{k_w} = -mN_p + \ln a. \quad \dots\dots\dots\dots\dots\dots\dots\dots\dots\dots\dots\dots\dots\dots \quad (7.5)$$

The two outcome coefficients representing the straightline interpretation of the k_o/k_w curve are the slope, m, and the intercept, $\ln a$, terms, which in turn may be included in Eq. 7.5 to calculate a relative-permeability-cumulative-production relationship.

The next step of the development shows how these coefficients are determined from another (different) straightline approximation constructed from field performance data.

Development of the X Plot Method. Rearrange Eq. 7.5 to the following exponential expression:

$$\frac{k_o}{k_w} = a\exp\left(-mN_p\right). \quad \dots\dots\dots\dots\dots\dots\dots\dots\dots\dots\dots\dots\dots\dots \quad (7.6)$$

Combining Eq. 7.6 with the fractional flow equation, Eq. 7.4, results in the following:

$$f_w = \frac{1}{1 + \dfrac{\mu_w}{\mu_o}\exp\left(-mN_p\right)}. \quad \dots\dots\dots\dots\dots\dots\dots\dots\dots\dots\dots\dots \quad (7.7)$$

Eq. 7.7 relates the fraction of water flowing in an oil-water system as a function of the oil-/water-viscosity ratio and the relative-permeability ratio curve. The Welge (1952) frontal-advance theory was applied to develop Eq. 7.8. The equation shows that water saturation at any point in time is a function of recovery efficiency, fraction of water flowing, and the slope of the straightline approximation of the relative-permeability ratio curve. Ershaghi and Omorigie (1978) discuss the derivation in greater detail.

$$S_w = E_R\left(1 - S_{wi}\right) + S_{wi} - \frac{1}{mf_w}. \quad \dots\dots\dots\dots\dots\dots\dots\dots\dots\dots\dots \quad (7.8)$$

Define recovery efficiency as the fractional displacement efficiency of the flood. Therefore, the recovery efficiency equation is as follows:

$$E_R = \frac{\text{Cumulative oil produced, STB}}{\text{Original oil in place, STB}}. \quad \dots\dots\dots\dots\dots\dots\dots\dots\dots\dots\dots \quad (7.9)$$

Remember, recovery efficiency is the product of the reservoir vertical and areal displacement efficiencies. Vertical sweep efficiency is essentially a function of the degree of reservoir layering and/or the effectiveness of gravity segregation. A homogeneous sand possesses a vertical sweep efficiency of unity if the effect of gravity does not cause appreciable segregation of the oil and water. Well pattern and density, sequence of well completions, and any changes of reservoir character define areal sweep.

Combining Eq. 7.9 with Eq. 7.8 and rearranging for the recovery efficiency term to be plotted on the x axis results in Eq. 7.10.

$$\left[\ln\left(\frac{1}{f_w}-1\right)-\frac{1}{f_w}\right]=\left[m\left(1-S_{wi}\right)\right]E_R+\left[mS_{wi}-\ln\left(a\frac{\mu_w}{\mu_o}\right)\right]. \quad\dots\dots\dots\dots\dots\dots \quad (7.10)$$

Include the f_w-WOR (Eq. 7.3) and S_w-N_p relationships, and arrange Eq. 7.10 in the form of the equation of a straight line. Note: The slope and intercept coefficients defining this straightline approximation of the performance curve are different from those established for the relative-permeability ratio curve. Plotting components for this straightline approximation are as follows:

y plotting variable: $\left|\ln \text{OWR} - \text{OWR} - 1\right|.$ $\dots\dots\dots\dots\dots\dots\dots\dots\dots\dots\dots$ (7.11)

x plotting variable: $N_p.$ $\dots\dots\dots\dots\dots\dots\dots\dots\dots\dots\dots\dots\dots\dots\dots\dots$ (7.12)

Note: The ordinate plotting variable is determined as the absolute magnitude of the argument, $\ln(\text{OWR})$–OWR–1. The arguments of the y axis plotting variable values are inherently always negative, yet the ordinate scale plotting variable values are positive.

The outcome variables of the X plot are the slope and intercept coefficients. Note: Eqs. 7.13 and 7.14 contain the slope and intercept coefficients for a relative-permeability curve. Note that the expression given in Eq. 7.13 for the slope (n) is derived from the first term on the right side of Eq. 7.10.

Outcome variable: Slope: $n = m(1 - S_{wi}).$ $\dots\dots\dots\dots\dots\dots\dots\dots\dots\dots\dots$ (7.13)

Rearrange Eq. 7.13 to solve for the slope of the straight line of the k_o/k_w curve.

Slope of the k_o/k_w vs. S_w curve: $m = \dfrac{n}{(1 - S_{wi})}.$ $\dots\dots\dots\dots\dots\dots\dots\dots\dots\dots\dots$ (7.14)

Note that the y-intercept outcome variable (c) in this analysis derives directly from Eq. 7.10 (the last term on the right side is the intercept). This variable is therefore given by Eq. 7.15.

Outcome variable: y intercept: $c = mS_{wi} - \ln\left(a\dfrac{\mu_w}{\mu_o}\right).$ $\dots\dots\dots\dots\dots\dots\dots\dots\dots\dots$ (7.15)

Rearrange Eq. 7.15 to solve for the intercept of the straight line of the k_o/k_w curve.

Intercept of the k_o/k_w vs. S_w curve: $a = \dfrac{\mu_o}{\mu_w}\exp\left(mS_{wi} - c\right).$ $\dots\dots\dots\dots\dots\dots\dots\dots\dots$ (7.16)

Estimating ultimate recovery with exactitude for a heterogeneous system usually poses a very difficult, if not impossible, problem because of the uncertainties in reservoir character. Therefore, cumulative recovery values usually replace the recovery efficiency term. This replacement is logical, because the OOIP does not change even though one may be uncertain of its true value. Ershaghi and Abdassah (1984) showed that the results of the calculations are the same if the X plot is constructed with the water-cut term placed on the y axis (Ershaghi and Abdassah 1984). The form of the plot and the location of the components of the straight line are shown in **Fig. 7.10.**

7.3.2 The k_o/k_w Field Curve. Relative-permeability ratios developed from the X plot are field or composite relative-permeability ratios because the effect of the transmissibility distribution, well spacing, and field operations are incorporated into the plot's shape. These curves should be combined with geological studies to interpret future performance and provide input for more sophisticated reservoir engineering models. A par-

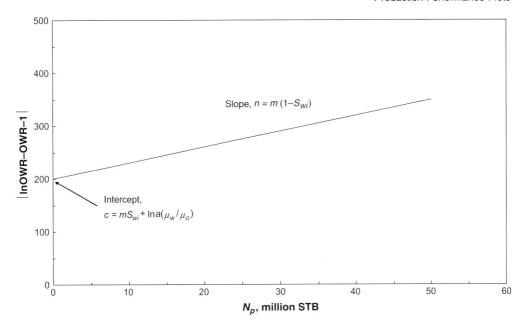

Fig. 7.10—An example of the X plot. Include the slope and intercept values interpreted from the figure into Eq. 7.6 to calculate the k_o/k_w curve particular to these field conditions.

ticularly useful application is to combine field relative-permeability ratios with geological models to characterize the reservoir flow system.

Relative-permeability curves determined from field performance data should represent the field character no matter how "imperfect" their nature. The following discussion develops the ability of the X plot method to define the field curve.

7.3.3 Calculation Procedure.
Apply field data to generate an X plot to initiate the analysis procedure and draw a straightline approximation through the data points. Apply the slope and intercept coefficients interpreted from the straight line to construct a relative-permeability ratio curve. Data requirements are production information, average viscosity of the two fluids, and the initial water saturation. The procedure is as follows:

Plot the production data. Use OWR in Eq. 7.11 and cumulative production values to construct the X plot.

Interpret the straightline slope and intercept values. Scan the figure to determine the best straight line(s). Approximating the production history with straight lines should be done with a straight edge and not with a curve-fitting equation. There is generally more than one obvious straight line. Calculate the slope and intercept values of each of the interpreted straight lines and the cumulative production values over which this straight line is evident.

Find the slope and intercept values for the relative-permeability ratio curve. Apply Eqs. 7.14 and 7.15.

Slope of the k_o/k_w vs. S_w curve: $m = \dfrac{n}{(1 - S_{wi})}$.

Outcome variable: y intercept: $c = mS_{wi} - \ln\left(a\,\dfrac{\mu_w}{\mu_o}\right)$.

Apply the two coefficients determined in the previous step to construct the k_o/k_w-S_w curve or for inclusion into Eqs. 7.5 or 7.6 to express the straight line in equation form. This analysis procedure develops a WOR-k_o/k_w-cumulative-production relationship spanning that particular period of the production history.

Development of the previous derivation assumed a homogeneous sand waterflooded under constant operating conditions. An extension to this work would be to study the effect of layering on the X plot.

7.3.4 Effect of Layering and Field Operations. The shape of the X plot reflects the degree of differential fluid movement in a layered reservoir as the displacing fluid encroaches into the sand members. The total system throughput is the sum of the interaction of the transmissibilities of the individual layers. Variables included in the equations are the viscosity ratio, thickness, and effective permeability of each layer. The first two variables are assumed to remain constant, while the relative-permeability ratios constantly change. Therefore, changes in the straight line of the plot should reflect changes in the field or composite relative-permeability ratio.

Fig. 7.11 is an idealized X plot for a hypothetical three-layer system. The form of the plot is similar to the results of studies by Ershaghi et al. (1987) and Snyder and Ramey (1967). Three distinct straight lines are apparent in the performance plot. Each straight line includes the cumulative effects of the individual layers if one assumes that field operations do not change. The first curve during Period 1 is a composite of the relative-permeability ratios of the three layers flowing mainly oil. The curve covering Period 2 reflects the permeability-to-oil effects of the middle- and least-permeable layers, while the curve for Period 3 reflects the permeability-to-oil effects of the least-permeable layer coupled with the composite water-permeability effects of the three layers. These relations become more apparent when one realizes that water initially breaks through in the highest-permeability layer. Subsequent water breakthroughs occur in a descending order of layer transmissibility. The figure is similar to the figure by Prats et al. (1959) shown as Fig. 7.5. The displacement process is becoming more inefficient with time, because more water is produced per unit volume of produced oil.

A paper by Ershaghi et al. (1987) developed a relationship between the X plot and the volume of water injected. A reservoir study of the characteristics of the Sidi El-Itayem reservoir in Tunisia was used to illustrate the usefulness of this concept. The field is composed of a three-layer carbonate system transected by faults. The problem was to use production data to determine the area swept by the natural waterdrive process.

All the work published on the X plot method applies to the last or only a single straight line to predict performance. Note: This assumption is unwarranted. All types of semilog cumulative-production water-cut plots usually exhibit more than one straightline approximation during differing portions of the production history. Why should the last straight line present a better estimate of future performance than the previous one if additional layers in the reservoir are expected to become flooded out? It is probably closer to the prediction, but by how much? A simple mathematical calculation does not provide a complete answer.

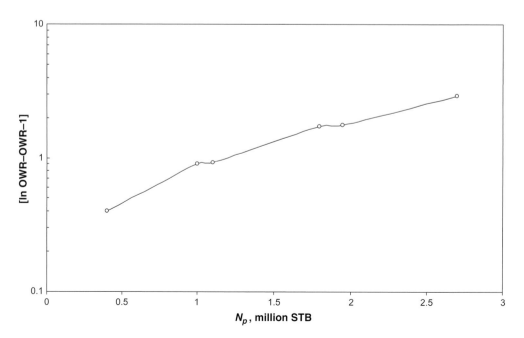

Fig. 7.11—The X plot for a hypothetical three-layer system. Note the three distinct periods representing water breakthrough to the producing wells as the lesser transmissibility layers are gradually flooded out.

   Prediction of performance by analyzing the last straightline approximation displayed by a heterogeneous reservoir should always present an optimistic picture of expectations, because one expects the slope of the last and presently unknown straight line to be flatter than the projections from the historical data. Therefore, future oil-water relationships will be overstated if the last historical straightline approximation is used in the prediction; however, it can provide insight into reservoir behavior. Analysis of these curves, in conjunction with a geological review, can provide a better picture of the field-displacement process.

   Fig. 7.12 shows two of the well history plots with interpretations of at least two straight lines for each instance.

   Example. Apply the X plot solution procedure to the previously discussed example problem of the multi-layered oil reservoir. The reservoir performance history and WOR and OWR plots are shown in Figs. 7.7 and 7.8. **Table 7.1** lists the reservoir properties.

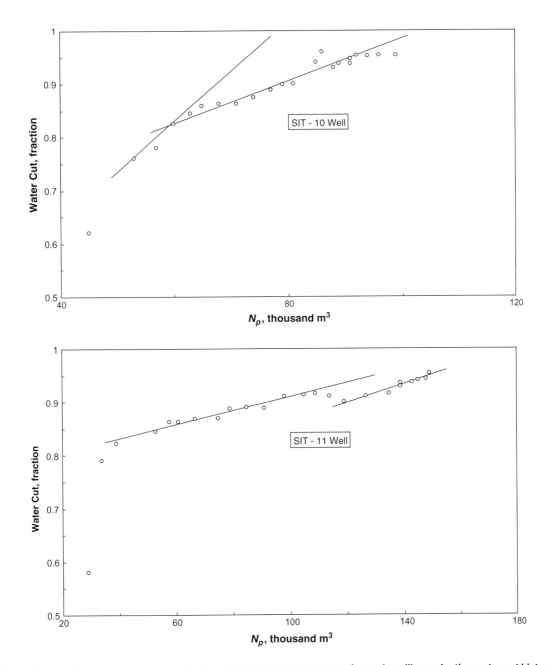

Fig. 7.12—Well history plots for two wells. Two straight lines are apparent for each well's production water-cut history.

TABLE 7.1—RESERVOIR PROPERTIES: EXAMPLE FIELD		
S_{wi}= 23%	ϕ = 33%	S_{or}= 31%
μ_w = 1.0 cp	μ_o = 9.3 cp	B_o= 1.06 RB/STB

The field data were entered into Eqs. 7.11 and 7.12 to generate the X plot. The resulting U-shaped graph is shown in **Fig. 7.13.** Two obvious straight lines and probably one subsidiary line can represent the plot. These straight lines reflect the field relative-permeability ratio curves operating during different time periods. The steeper slope, Curve 2, indicates the presence of a less-efficient oil-displacement process because more water is flowing in relation to the unit volume of oil recovered. The strange behavior of the early-time data and commonly observed multiple straight lines is not discussed by Ershaghi et al. (1987) and Snyder and Ramey (1967).

The following presents the calculation procedure for analyzing the Period 1 approximation:

Calculate slope and intercept values of the straightline approximation. The straight line for Period 1 spans the 24- to 42-million-STB cumulative-production period.

Read the intercept at the point where the straight line crosses the y axis: $c = 1.03$.

$$\text{Slope: } n = \frac{y_2 - y_1}{x_2 - x_1} = \frac{3.10 - 1.87}{(50 - 20) \text{ million STB}} = 0.041/\text{million STB}.$$

Calculate the slope and intercept values to construct the field k_o/k_w curve. Apply Eq. 7.14 to calculate the slope of the straight line.

$$m = \frac{n}{1 - S_{wi}} = \frac{0.041}{1 - 0.23} = 0.053/\text{million STB}.$$

Apply Eq. 7.16 to determine the intercept value for the relative-permeability ratio curve.

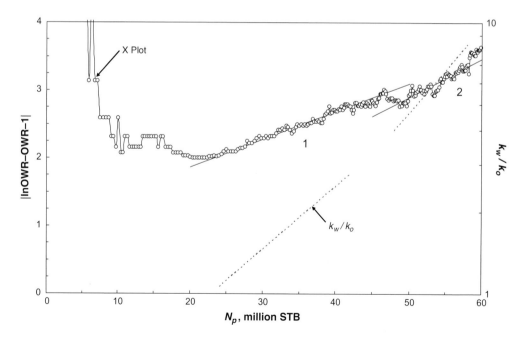

Fig. 7.13—Example problem X plot results. The algebraic relation between the arithmetic and logarithmic OWR values included in Eq. 7.11 at high- and low-water-cut values causes this pronounced and characteristic U shape. Nevertheless, two straightline approximations are apparent. Note: The resulting water/oil relative-permeability ratio curves are also plotted on this figure.

$$a = \frac{\mu_o}{\mu_w}\exp(mS_{wi} - c) = \frac{9.3}{1.0}\exp\left[(0.053)(0.23) - 1.03\right] = 3.36.$$

Substitute the coefficients developed in the previous steps into Eq. 7.6 to form the field relative-permeability ratio curve applicable during the 24- to 42-million-STB production period.

$$\frac{k_o}{k_w} = 3.36\exp\left(-0.053N_p\right)$$

The slope and the intercept values for the Periods 1 and 2 interpretations with their resulting relative-permeability ratio equations are shown in **Table 7.2.**

The endpoints of the relative-permeability ratio curve. The cumulative-recovery values are defined as the beginning, and endpoints for the Period 1 are included in the previous equation to calculate the field relative-permeability ratio endpoints. The 42-million-STB endpoint is calculated in a similar manner.

$$\frac{k_o}{k_w} = 3.36\exp\left(-0.053N_p\right) = 3.36\exp\left[(-0.053)(24)\right] = 0.94$$

The endpoints for both periods listed in Table 7.2 are plotted as the right scale in Fig. 7.13. Note: The inverse-permeability ratio, k_w/k_o, is plotted in the figure to mirror the WOR response. The two curves highlight the dramatic loss of the ability of the reservoir to flow oil because of the "flooding out" of the highest-permeability sand members.

The problems with using the X plot method are the somewhat cumbersome calculation procedure, the $f_w >$ 0.5 requirement, and the strange behavior of the early-time data. The next section develops a more straightforward and versatile technique.

7.4 The Fluid Ratio Plotting Method

Lo et al. (1990) indicated that a produced-fluid ratio cumulative-production plot dispensed with the early-time problems inherent with the X plot method. The following discussion applies this concept to develop relative-permeability ratio curves for a water-displacing-oil system. However, the same method can easily be extended to gas-displacing-oil and water-displacing-gas systems.

7.4.1 Assumptions and Concept Development. Assume the existence of a straightline semilog k_o/k_w vs. N_p relationship. Rearrange and take the logarithm of both sides of the combined fractional flow and relative-permeability ratio equation, Eq. 7.7, expressed in terms of cumulative production.

$$-mN_p = -\ln\left(a\frac{\mu_w}{\mu_o}\right) + \ln\left(\frac{1}{f_w} - 1\right). \quad\dots\dots\dots\dots\dots\dots\dots\dots (7.17)$$

TABLE 7.2—COMPONENTS OF THE X PLOT: EXAMPLE PROBLEM			
Range Recovery (million STB)	X Plot c	X Plot n (1/million STB)	k_o/k_w Curve Equation
24–42	1.03	0.041	$\frac{k_o}{k_w} = 3.36\exp(-0.053\,N_p)$ Range (0.94 – 0.36)
48–58	0.12	0.056	$\frac{k_o}{k_w} = 8.39\exp(-0.073\,N_p)$ Range (0.25 – 0.12)

Substituting the f_w-WOR relationship (Eq. 7.3) and the WOR-OWR relationships and rearranging the result yields the following:

$$\ln OWR = \ln\left(a\frac{\mu_w}{\mu_o}\right) - mN_p. \quad\dots\dots\dots\dots\dots\dots\dots\dots\dots\dots\dots\dots\dots\dots\dots \quad (7.18)$$

Rearrange Eq. 7.18 to the form of an equation of a straight line with a negative slope. The plotting components of the line are as follows:

y plotting variable: $\ln OWR$. $\dots\dots\dots\dots\dots\dots\dots\dots\dots\dots\dots\dots\dots\dots\dots\dots\dots\dots$ (7.19)

x plotting variable: N_p. $\dots\dots\dots\dots\dots\dots\dots\dots\dots\dots\dots\dots\dots\dots\dots\dots\dots\dots\dots\dots$ (7.20)

The two outcome coefficients representing the slope and intercepts of the straightline interpretation are as follows:

Outcome coefficient: Slope of the line: $-m$. $\dots\dots\dots\dots\dots\dots\dots\dots\dots\dots\dots\dots\dots\dots\dots$ (7.21)

Outcome coefficient: y intercept: $\ln\left(a\frac{\mu_w}{\mu_o}\right)$. $\dots\dots\dots\dots\dots\dots\dots\dots\dots\dots\dots\dots\dots\dots\dots$ (7.22)

The slope of the straightline approximation of the oil-to-water relative-permeability ratio is similar to the k_o/k_w curve shown in Fig. 7.1. This similar relationship indicates that the logarithm of the OWR and the field k_o/k_w expressions display similar properties and are interchangeable.

The fluid ratio plotting method does not include the frontal-advance equation. However, the range of application has been extended when compared to the Ershaghi method.

7.4.2 Calculation Procedure. Data requirements are historical production records, and the average viscosity of each of the two fluids flowing in the system. The analysis procedure is as follows:

Plot the production data. Construct a semilog plot of OWR vs. N_p.

Interpret the performance plot. Draw best-fit straight line(s) through the data plot, and interpret the slope and intercept values for each.

Develop the relative-permeability ratio curve. The slope of the straightline approximation of the performance plot represents the slope of the field or composite k_o/k_w curve, Eq. 7.21. Eq. 7.22 defines the intercept of the k_o/k_w curve.

y intercept: $\ln\left(a\frac{\mu_w}{\mu_o}\right)$

Apply these coefficients to develop the field k_o/k_w curve applicable during this particular production period. Apply Eq. 7.6 to develop the field relative-permeability ratio equation.

$$\frac{k_o}{k_w} = a\exp\left(-mN_p\right)$$

Example. The example problem discussed in the two previous sections of this chapter is used to illustrate the utility of this concept. The previously discussed semilog OWR vs. N_p plot shown in Fig. 7.8 was constructed from the performance data.

Five straightline approximations are evident. Period 1 probably occurs during the primary waterflood phase because water injection was initiated after 5 million STB had been produced. Periods 2 and 3, and probably 4, represent the waterflood phase after initial water breakthrough. Period 5 appears to represent a time when field operations became less efficient, and water production became more pronounced.

The intercept and slope values for each of the straight lines were determined. Eqs. 7.21 and 7.22 are applied to calculate the slope and intercept of the k_o/k_w curve appropriate to each particular cumulative-production group. The following illustrates the calculation procedure for Period 1.

Estimate the k_o/k_w slope and intercept values. The straight line extends over the 5- to 11-million-STB cumulative production range and crosses the y axis at ln(18). This value is included in Eq. 7.22 to calculate the intercept value of the relative-permeability ratio curve.

$$\text{Intercept} = \ln\left(a\frac{\mu_w}{\mu_o}\right): \quad \ln(18) = \ln a\left(\frac{1}{9.3}\right): \quad a = 167.4$$

The slope of the relative-permeability ratio curve is the negative value of the slope of the OWR line.

$$m = \frac{y_2 - y_1}{x_2 - x_1} = \frac{\ln 1.04 - \ln 7.8}{12 - 3.5} = \frac{0.04 - 2.05}{8.5} = -0.237$$

TABLE 7.3—COMPONENTS OF THE OWR PLOT AND RESULTING RELATIVE-PERMEABILITY CURVES

Flow Period	N_p Range (million STB)	WOR Range (STB/STB)	Intercept (STB/STB)	Slope (1/million STB)	k_o/k_w Equation
1	5–11	0.2–0.5	18	−0.237	167.4 exp(−0.237 N_p)
2	16–29	0.5–2.3	12	−0.114	111.6 exp(−0.114 N_p)
3	30–39	2.3–4.0	2.2	−0.054	20.5 exp(−0.054 N_p)
4	39–47	4.4–5.4	0.83	−0.033	7.7 exp(−0.033 N_p)
5	52–58	6.7–12.5	14	−0.083	130.2 exp(−0.033 N_p)

at $N_p = 5$: $\dfrac{k_o}{k_w} = 167.4 \exp(-0.237 N_p) = 51.2$, $\dfrac{k_w}{k_o} = 0.02$

at $N_p = 11$: $\dfrac{k_o}{k_w} = 167.4 \exp(-0.237 N_p) = 12.3$, $\dfrac{k_w}{k_o} = 0.08$

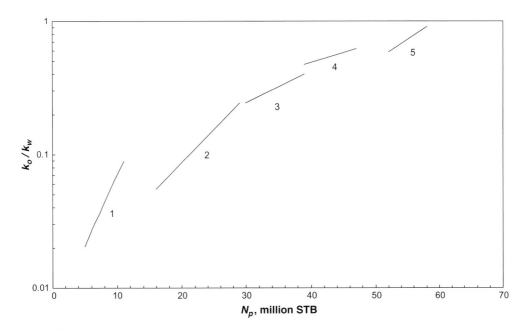

Fig. 7.14—The relative-permeability ratio plot: example problem. Note: The ability of water to flow in preference to oil increases over time, and Period 5 appears to display an even more inefficient process.

The slope and intercept coefficients are included in Eq. 7.6 to form the relative-permeability ratio equation for the Period 1 timespan.

$$\frac{k_o}{k_w} = 167.4 \exp\left(-0.237 N_p\right)$$

Calculate the k_o/k_w endpoints. The endpoints listed in **Table 7.3** are input into the Period 1 relative-permeability ratio equation to calculate the maximum and minimum relative-permeability ratio values.

The equations of all the relative-permeability ratio curves with their appropriate endpoints for each period were calculated in a similar manner. The results of these efforts are listed in Table 7.3. The calculated relative-permeability ratio (k_w/k_o) curves are shown in **Fig. 7.14.** Note: There is an orderly progression of the changing relative-permeability curves with production history for the middle three time periods.

The slope of the k_o/k_w curve for the primary decline Period 1 is clearly steeper than observed in the other curves. The high fluid-transmission rates in the more permeable sands cause the dramatic falloff of the oil production rate immediately after water breakthrough in these sands. The slope of the Period 1 curve reflects rapidly increasing water production. The k_o/k_w curves for Periods 3 and 4 appear to be an extension of the Period 2 k_o/k_w curve. The decreasing slope is caused by the encroaching water gradually displacing oil in the lower-permeability layers. Period 5 does not fit the "norm" of the first four periods.

Chapter 8

Recent Developments in Decline-Curve Analyses

A number of recent advances have been made in the technology of production decline-curve analyses. These enhancements resulted in improvements in the interpretation of production decline performance data over the decline-curve analysis techniques traditionally used. Palacio and Blasingame (1993) demonstrated that the equivalent of the Horner approximation of the pseudoproduction time function was useful for correlating the production decline behavior of a well with a varying flow rate history to classical production decline-curve solutions. Doublet and Blasingame (1995a) demonstrated that a theoretically sound basis could be established for coupling the transient and boundary-dominated flow stems of the production decline behavior of a well to obtain a composite decline-curve set that is readily applicable for graphical production decline analyses. Agarwal et al. (1999) subsequently used these two concepts in a production analysis methodology that included decline-curve and boundary-dominated, flow-specialized analyses.

Another important enhancement of the classical production decline curve analysis technology introduced in recent years is the use of integral and derivative production decline functions (Doublet et al. 1994) to reduce the uniqueness problems that are commonly encountered in graphical production decline-curve analyses. The integral and derivative functions are used in combination with the standard flow rate decline function to better identify the appropriate transient flow decline stem for production behavior of a well.

Composite production decline-curve sets have also been developed for a number of well types and outer-boundary conditions. Among these sets are production decline curves for infinite-conductivity vertically fractured (Doublet and Blasingame 1995a) and horizontal wells (Shih and Blasingame 1995), and unfractured vertical wells with specified water influx across the external boundary (Doublet and Blasingame 1995b). Production decline curves for finite-conductivity vertical fractures have also been developed using the techniques discussed by Doublet and Blasingame (1995a).

8.1 Horner Approximation of the Pseudoproducing Time

A production decline-curve analysis technique has also been reported in the Poe (2002) literature for considering the case in which a complete production data set, consisting of both the flow rates and well-flowing pressures at each time level, is unavailable. In that case, a conventional convolution analysis cannot be employed to properly consider the effects of a varying well-flowing pressure and flow rate history on the production decline behavior of a well. In cases such as this, an equivalent convolution analysis can be used that consists of a hybrid convolution methodology that directly relates the Horner approximation of the pseudoproduction time function to the conventional superposition time.

8.1.1 Material Balance Time Concept.
Palacio and Blasingame (1993) demonstrated that an approximate decline time function developed by McCray (1990) was useful for correlating the varying flow rate production decline performance of a well with the classical decline-curve solutions. This approximate decline time function was referred to as the "material balance" time function. It can be readily observed that the decline time function used in the Palacio and Blasingame (1993) study is completely analogous to the Horner

approximation of the pseudoproducing time function traditionally used in pressure-transient analyses to approximate the effect of a varying flow rate history on the shut-in pressure-transient response of a well. Therefore, either name for this production decline time function can be used interchangeably with the other because they are identical. This approximate decline time function is simply the equivalent production time value resulting from the ratio of the cumulative production to the flow rate of a well at a given point in time. The decline time function applicable for a single-phase oil-reservoir analysis is expressed mathematically in consistent units in Eq. 8.1.

$$t_{mb}(t) = \frac{N_p(t)}{q_o(t)}. \quad \dots\dots\dots\dots\dots\dots\dots\dots\dots\dots\dots\dots\dots\dots\dots\dots\dots\dots\dots\dots\dots\dots\dots \text{(8.1)}$$

Similarly, the corresponding decline time function applicable for single-phase gas-reservoir analyses is given in consistent units in Eq. 8.2.

$$t_{mb}(t) = \frac{G_p(t)}{q_g(t)}. \quad \dots\dots\dots\dots\dots\dots\dots\dots\dots\dots\dots\dots\dots\dots\dots\dots\dots\dots\dots\dots\dots\dots\dots \text{(8.2)}$$

For multiphase liquid flow cases (i.e., significant production of oil and brine), it is often necessary to consider a decline time function that includes the effects of the production of both liquids. In such cases, the decline time function given in consistent units in Eq. 8.3 is preferred.

$$t_{mb}(t) = \frac{N_p(t)B_o + W_p(t)B_w}{q_o(t)B_o + q_w(t)B_w}. \quad \dots\dots\dots\dots\dots\dots\dots\dots\dots\dots\dots\dots\dots\dots\dots\dots\dots \text{(8.3)}$$

8.1.2 Assumptions and Limitations. The Horner approximation of the pseudoproduction time (i.e., material balance time) function used in the production decline analyses given in Palacio and Blasingame (1993), Doublet and Blasingame (1995a, 1995b), Agarwal et al. (1999), Doublet et al. (1994), and Shih and Blasingame (1995) is subject to a number of assumptions and limitations. First, its use does not have a theoretical basis; it is purely intuitive. As originally noted by Horner (1951), when this production time approximation was first proposed for use in pressure buildup analyses of wells with varying flow rate histories, the accuracy of this time function approximation as a substitute for the superposition-in-time function equivalent is restricted to a smoothly varying flow rate history. This requirement also applies to production decline analyses of variable flow rate histories and has been verified by the investigations of Winestock and Colpitts (1965) and Lee et al. (1972). Therefore, a highly varying and erratic flow rate history shortly before the time of interest adversely affects the accuracy of the approximation.

Another extremely important factor related to the accuracy of the Horner approximation of the pseudoproduction time for estimation of the equivalent superposition time function is the apparent steady-state skin effect of the well. As Poe and Mahaendrajana (2002) have shown, the material balance and superposition time functions for the early rate-transient performance of a well with a finite-conductivity vertical fracture in an infinite-acting reservoir can differ by as much as 200% during the pseudolinear (or formation linear) flow regime. This difference is illustrated in **Fig. 8.1** for a wide range of dimensionless fracture conductivities.

Note: During the pseudolinear (or formation linear) flow regime (exhibited in the transient performance of moderate-to-high dimensionless conductivity fractures), the ratio of the material balance to superposition time functions is equal to 2. Similarly, during the bilinear flow regime of a finite-conductivity fracture, the material balance time is 33% greater than the actual superposition time (i.e., factor of 4/3). However, of even greater concern is the fact that during the early transient behavior of finite-conductivity vertical fractures, the relationship between the material balance and superposition time functions is continuously varying. The flux distribution in the fracture stabilizes once the fully developed pseudoradial flow regime of a finite-conductivity vertically fractured well has been exhibited in the transient performance of the well. At that point, a meaningful relationship between these two time functions can be developed and achieves a stable and essentially constant value.

In general, it has been demonstrated that the Horner approximation of the pseudoproduction time function is always greater than or equal to the corresponding superposition time function (Poe 2003) at a given time level. This inequality is expressed mathematically in Eq. 8.4 in terms of dimensionless variables and holds

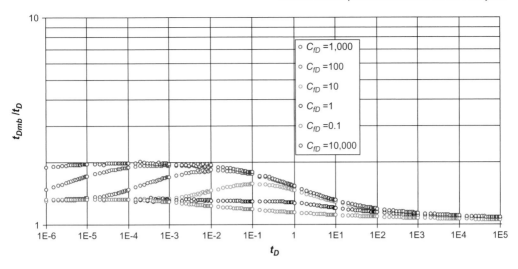

Fig. 8.1—Relationship between the material balance and superposition time functions for a finite-conductivity vertical fracture in an infinite-acting reservoir.

for all well types (i.e., vertical or slanted unfractured, vertically fractured, and horizontal wells) at all time levels and for all flow regimes.

$$t_{Dmb}(t) \geq t_D(t). \qquad (8.4)$$

The complete details of the development of the fundamental relationships between the material balance and superposition time functions for each of the transient flow regimes of a finite-conductivity vertical fracture are discussed by Poe (2005) for both rate and pressure-transient analyses. Rate-transient-based production-decline analyses are more appropriate for the evaluation of the production-performance behavior of a well than are analyses derived using pressure-transient solutions for a number of reasons, many of which are given by Poe (2002, 2003, 2005) and Poe and Marhaendrajana (2002). Thus, only the rate-transient analysis approach is further considered in this text. However, the corresponding development for the pressure-transient analyses of a vertically fractured well is summarized by Poe (2005).

For rate-transient analyses, the dimensionless material balance time function is directly related to the ratio of the dimensionless cumulative production and the dimensionless well flow rate, given in Eq. 8.5. Note the similarity of this expression with those given for the dimensional material balance time functions of Eqs. 8.1 through 8.3.

$$t_{Dmb}(t) = \frac{Q_{pD}(t)}{q_{wD}(t)}. \qquad (8.5)$$

The dimensionless material balance time function is defined in consistent units with Eq. 8.6.

$$t_{Dmb}(t) = \frac{k\, t_{mb}(t)}{\phi \mu c_t L_c^2}. \qquad (8.6)$$

The characteristic length of the system under consideration (L_c) is equal to half the source/sink lateral extent in the reservoir. For example, the system characteristic length of an unfractured vertical well is equal to half the wellbore diameter (i.e., the well radius). For a vertically fractured well, the system characteristic length is equal to half the total fracture length in the reservoir (i.e., the fracture half-length). Similarly, the system characteristic length of a horizontal well is equal to half the total effective wellbore length in the reservoir ($L_c = L_h/2$).

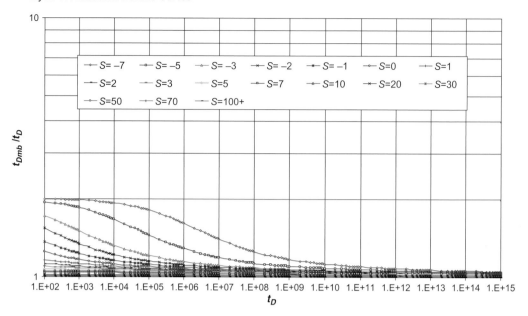

Fig. 8.2—Relationship between the material balance and superposition time functions for an unfractured vertical well in an infinite-acting reservoir.

Analogous to the relationship between the material balance and superposition time functions for a well with a finite-conductivity vertical fracture given in Fig. 8.1, a similar graphical depiction of the relationship between these two time functions for a fully penetrating, unfractured, finite-wellbore vertical well with differing apparent steady-state skin effects (Poe 2003) is given in **Fig. 8.2.** Note: The relationship between these two time functions for the case of a large negative skin effect ($S = -7$) becomes asymptotic to a value of 2 at early time. From the apparent wellbore radius concept, this level of well stimulation is equivalent to that which one would expect for a well intersected by an infinite-conductivity vertical fracture during the formation linear flow regime. Note this value in Fig. 8.1. In Fig. 8.2, it is observed that the only case in which the material balance and superposition time functions for an unfractured well are identical for all time levels is for a heavily damaged well ($S=100+$).

An even more complex relationship exists between these two time functions for the early transient behavior of an infinite-conductivity horizontal well (Poe 2003), as demonstrated in **Fig. 8.3.** This example illustration of the relationship between the material balance and superposition time functions for an infinite-conductivity horizontal well was prepared for the case of a horizontal well centrally positioned midway between the upper and lower no-flow boundaries of the reservoir and with a dimensionless wellbore radius (i.e., relative to the net pay thickness of the reservoir, $r_{wD}=r_w/h$) of 0.003. All the variation in the relationship between the two time functions presented in Fig. 8.3 for the various dimensionless wellbore lengths ($L_D=L_h/2h$) occur before the development of the second pseudoradial flow period, a flow regime that would be analogous to the pseudoradial flow period commonly considered in vertically fractured well-transient behaviors.

8.2 Correction of Material Balance Time in Decline-Curve Analyses

The Horner approximation of the pseudoproduction time function can be readily computed from the historical production performance of a well using the appropriate relationship given in Eqs. 8.1 through 8.3 for the reservoir type under consideration. The ease with which this decline time function can be evaluated made it quite popular for production decline-curve analyses (Palacio and Blasingame 1993; Doublet and Blasingame 1995a, 1995b; Agarwal et al. 1999; Doublet et al. 1994; Shih and Blasingame 1995). However, as previously discussed, a simple substitution of the material balance time in place of the superposition time function can result in a significant error in the production analysis of the early transient behavior of most well types.

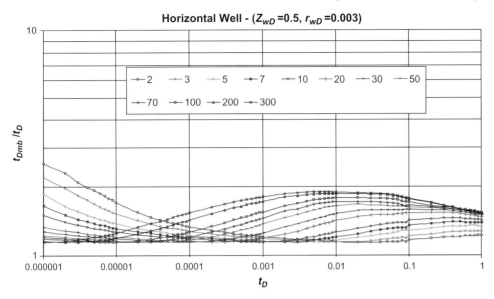

Fig. 8.3—Relationship between the material balance and superposition time functions for an infinite-conductivity horizontal well in an infinite-acting reservoir.

An improved and more accurate production decline analysis methodology can be constructed using the appropriate correction of the material balance time function to obtain a time function value equivalent to the superposition time of a varying rate history (Poe 2002, 2003, 2005; Poe and Marhaendrajana 2002). This is accomplished by using the fundamental definitions of the dimensional and dimensionless material balance time functions. The relationship between the dimensionless and dimensional material balance and superposition time functions is stated in Eq. 8.7. As a result, the multiplicative correction factor for the dimensional material balance time function is therefore obtained with Eq. 8.8, and the equivalent superposition time function value may be estimated from the material balance time using Eq. 8.9.

$$\frac{t_{mb}(t)}{t_e(t)} = \frac{t_{Dmb}(t)}{t_D(t)} = \frac{Q_{pD}(t)}{q_{wD}(t) t_D(t)}. \quad \dots \dots \dots \dots \dots \dots \dots \dots \dots \dots \dots \dots \dots \dots \dots (8.7)$$

$$\alpha = \frac{q_{wD}(t) t_D(t)}{Q_{pD}(t)}. \quad \dots \dots \dots \dots \dots \dots \dots \dots \dots \dots \dots \dots \dots \dots \dots \dots \dots \dots \dots \dots (8.8)$$

$$t_e(t) = \alpha t_{mb}(t). \quad \dots \dots \dots \dots \dots \dots \dots \dots \dots \dots \dots \dots \dots \dots \dots \dots \dots \dots \dots \dots \dots \dots \dots (8.9)$$

The dimensionless superposition time is defined in a manner similar to that used for the dimensionless material balance time, except that it relates the superposition time function of a variable flow rate history to its equivalent for a constant drawdown pressure (i.e., inner-boundary condition) history. This expression is given in Eq. 8.10.

$$t_D(t) = \frac{k t_e(t)}{\phi \mu c_t L_c^2}. \quad \dots \dots \dots \dots \dots \dots \dots \dots \dots \dots \dots \dots \dots \dots \dots \dots \dots \dots \dots \dots \dots (8.10)$$

Note: The dimensionless flow rate and cumulative production as a function of the dimensionless time on the right side of Eq. 8.8 can be obtained using the appropriate rate-transient solution for the well and reservoir type of interest. These values can be computed in whatever manner desired, either with various analytic or numerical solution methods.

For the development of a useful and practical graphical decline-curve analysis methodology involving the use of the material balance time function as conventionally defined, it may be advantageous to construct the reference dimensionless decline-curve set on which the dimensional production data and material balance time function values are to be plotted with the correction factor included in the reference decline curves. In this way, the reference dimensionless decline curves on which the production decline data and material balance time function values correspond directly to the data functions used.

Problem. A vertically fractured well produced 55,000 STB of oil in 3 months of production. The well has had a varying flow rate production history during those 3 months, and the current production rate is 400 STB/D. Evaluate the material balance time of the variable flow rate history of the well after 3 months of production.

Solution. The material balance time is evaluated in this case with Eq. 8.1.

$$\text{The. } t_{mb}(t) = \frac{N_p(t)}{q_o(t)} = \frac{55,000}{400} = 137.5 \text{ days} = 3,300 \text{ hours.}$$

8.3 Composite Production Decline-Curve-Analysis Models

The development of useful reference production decline-curve sets with which to match the historical production decline behavior of a well, for use in reservoir and well characterization, requires that both the early-time (infinite-acting transient) and late-time (boundary-dominated flow) responses of the well be incorporated into a single-composite decline-curve set. Coupling of the transient and boundary-dominated flow stems may be accomplished in an empirical manner, such as used by Fetkovich et al. (1987) and Fetkovich (1980), or with a theoretical basis as used in Doublet and Blasingame (1995a, 1995b) and Shih and Blasingame (1995). The empirical approach was previously addressed in this text. In this chapter, a theoretical basis for coupling the transient and boundary-dominated flow production decline behaviors into a composite production decline-curve set is provided.

8.3.1 Transient and Boundary-Dominated Flow Stems. The production decline behavior of a well is governed by a number of variables, among which are the time level of interest and the specific properties of the reservoir and well completion. The transient behavior of the well is governed by the intrinsic properties of the reservoir and the well completion efficiency. The effects of a finite drainage areal extent of the reservoir do not affect the transient production decline behavior of the well. Examples of the properties of the reservoir that govern the early transient behavior of the well are its effective permeability, porosity, fluid saturations, and fluid and rock properties. The effects of a dual-permeability or dual-porosity system also are factors in the early transient behavior of the well. Some of the well-completion efficiency properties that affect the early transient behavior of the well are the system characteristic length (L_c), the fraction of the productive formation height that is open to flow to the well, near-well stimulation or damage, and the specific completion design efficiencies, such as those caused by perforations and gravel-pack completions. Other factors may also affect the early transient behavior of a well, such as inertial and/or multiphase flow in porous media that are flow-rate- or time-dependent.

The late-time boundary-dominated flow behavior of a well is also governed by the previously addressed reservoir and completion properties that govern the transient behavior of the well. However, the boundary-dominated flow behavior of the well is more predominantly governed by the reservoir drainage areal extent and shape, the location of the well within that drainage area, and the types of boundaries that exist along the perimeter of the drainage area of the well, just as the name denoted for this flow regime suggests. During the fully developed boundary-dominated flow regime, the effects of all boundaries of the reservoir are exhibited in the production decline behavior of the well. A unique production decline-curve analysis of the historical production performance of a well can actually only be obtained when at least some of the production performance history spans at least a portion of both the transient and boundary-dominated flow regimes.

8.3.2 Theoretical Basis for Coupling Stems. The development of a set of composite production decline curves for evaluating the reservoir and completion properties using solutions of the rate-transient behavior of a well in a finite closed reservoir is actually quite simple and straightforward. Doublet and Blasingame

(1995a) presented both pressure and rate-transient approaches for establishing the necessary ordinate and abscissa scaling parameters required to obtain conjugation of the transient and boundary-dominated flow regime production decline behavior stems. The rate-transient approach is more applicable and directly provides the required scale shift parameter values.

The dimensionless rate-transient behavior of any well type (e.g., unfractured vertical, vertically fractured, or horizontal well) located in a closed finite reservoir, during the late-time fully developed boundary-dominated flow regime, can be generalized in the form given by Eq. 8.11.

$$q_{wD}\left(t_D\right) = \frac{1}{\xi}\exp\left(\frac{-2\pi t_{DA}}{\xi}\right). \qquad (8.11)$$

Note: The dimensionless time referenced to drainage area (t_{DA}) is defined in terms of the dimensionless time (Eq. 8.10) and the dimensionless drainage area (A_D). The dimensionless time referenced to the drainage area is thus defined mathematically as given in Eq. 8.12.

$$t_{DA}\left(t\right) = \frac{t_D\left(t\right)}{A_D}. \qquad (8.12)$$

The dimensionless drainage area is simply the drainage area of the reservoir divided by the square of the system characteristic length as shown in Eq. 8.13.

$$A_D = \frac{A}{L_c^2}. \qquad (8.13)$$

The system imaging function (ξ) appearing in Eq. 8.11 is specific for a given set of well completion and reservoir properties and the well location. The mathematical definitions of the system imaging function for the more commonly considered well completion and reservoir types are presented in the discussion that follows in this chapter (Eqs. 8.20 through 8.36).

It is observed from Eq. 8.11 that construction of a dimensionless decline analysis reference decline rate variable and a dimensionless decline time function results in a collapse of the whole family of boundary-dominated flow production decline stems to a single decline stem for the late-time flow regime. The dimensionless decline analysis reference decline rate variable is the product of the dimensionless well flow rate and the system imaging function (ξ). The dimensionless decline time function is shown to conveniently incorporate the elements of the argument of the exponential function. The resulting dimensionless decline flow rate relationship obtained with this variable substitution is given by Eq. 8.14, and the corresponding definitions of the dimensionless decline flow rate and decline time reference functions are given by Eqs. 8.15 and 8.16, respectively.

$$q_{Dd}\left(t_{Dd}\right) = \exp\left(-t_{Dd}\right) \qquad \{\text{boundary-dominated flow}\}. \qquad (8.14)$$

$$q_{Dd} = \xi\, q_{wD}. \qquad (8.15)$$

$$t_{Dd} = \frac{2\pi}{\xi}t_{DA}. \qquad (8.16)$$

The dimensionless cumulative production during the boundary-dominated flow regime can also be generalized for the rate-transient production decline behavior for a well. The dimensionless cumulative production of a well (e.g., unfractured vertical, vertically fractured, or horizontal well) in a finite closed reservoir is described by Eq. 8.17 for boundary-dominated flow.

$$Q_{pD}\left(t_D\right) = \frac{A_D}{2\pi}\left[1 - \exp\left(\frac{-2\pi t_{DA}}{\xi}\right)\right]. \qquad (8.17)$$

In a manner similar to the variable substitutions performed with the flow rate decline relationship (Eq. 8.11), a dimensionless decline cumulative-production function can also be used that is consistent with the decline functions defined in Eqs. 8.15 and 8.16. Note: The definition of the dimensionless decline cumulative-production function is therefore an integration of the dimensionless decline flow rate with respect to the dimensionless decline time.

$$Q_{pDd}\left(t_{Dd}\right) = \int_{0}^{t_{Dd}} q_{Dd}\left(\tau\right)d\tau = \frac{2\pi Q_{pD}}{A_D} \qquad \left\{\text{all values of } t_{Dd}\right\}. \qquad (8.18)$$

$$Q_{pDd}\left(t_{Dd}\right) = 1 - \exp\left(-t_{Dd}\right) = 1 - q_{Dd}\left(t_{Dd}\right) \qquad \left\{\text{boundary-dominated flow}\right\}. \qquad (8.19)$$

The nondimensional image function (ξ) applicable for an unfractured vertical well centrally located in a closed, circular reservoir is given by Eq. 8.20.

$$\xi = \ln\left(r_{eD}\right) - \frac{3}{4}. \qquad (8.20)$$

The dimensionless drainage radius (r_{eD}) appearing in Eq. 8.20 is defined in the conventional manner as shown in Eq. 8.21.

$$r_{eD} = \frac{r_e}{L_c} = \frac{r_e}{r_w}. \qquad (8.21)$$

Similarly, the image function appropriate for a fully penetrating, unfractured vertical well located at a reservoir spatial position given by the coordinates (X_{wD}, Y_{wD}) in a closed, rectangular reservoir of dimensions X_{eD} by Y_{eD} [whose reference origin is located at the lower left corner of the rectangle (Poe 2003)] is given by Eq. 8.22. Dimensionless spatial parameters ($X_D, Y_D, X_{wD}, Y_{wD}, X_{eD}$, and Y_{eD}) are defined in this case as the ratio of the corresponding dimensional spatial dimensions (X, Y, X_w, Y_w, X_e, and Y_e) to the system characteristic length ($L_c = r_w$).

$$\xi = 2\pi \frac{Y_{eD}}{X_{eD}}\left(\frac{1}{3} - \frac{Y_D}{Y_{eD}} + \frac{Y_D^2 + Y_{wD}^2}{2Y_{eD}^2}\right) + 2\sum_{m=1}^{\infty}\frac{1}{m}\cos\left(\frac{m\pi X_{wD}}{X_{eD}}\right)\cos\left(\frac{m\pi X_D}{X_{eD}}\right)$$

$$\cdot \frac{\cosh\left[\dfrac{m\pi\left(Y_{eD} - |Y_D - Y_{wD}|\right)}{X_{eD}}\right] + \cosh\left[\dfrac{m\pi\left(Y_{eD} - (Y_D + Y_{wD})\right)}{X_{eD}}\right]}{\sinh\left(\dfrac{m\pi Y_{eD}}{X_{eD}}\right)}. \qquad (8.22)$$

The solution given in Eq. 8.22 can be recast into a more readily computable form (Eq. 8.23) in which the solution is derived for a spatial position of $(X_D = X_{wD}, Y_D = Y_{wD})$. Note: During the early transient behavior of a vertical well, the wellbore solution is commonly evaluated using a line source well solution at a dimensionless reservoir spatial position away from the center of the well equal to the dimensionless wellbore radius ($r_D = 1$). However, under boundary-dominated flow conditions, it is generally sufficient to simply evaluate the solution at the reservoir spatial position equal to the midpoint of the wellbore ($X_D = X_{wD}, Y_D = Y_{wD}$).

$$\xi = 2\pi \frac{Y_{eD}}{X_{eD}}\left(\frac{1}{3} - \frac{Y_{wD}}{Y_{eD}} + \frac{Y_{wD}^2}{Y_{eD}^2}\right) + 2\sum_{m=1}^{\infty}\frac{1}{m}\cos\left(\frac{m\pi X_{wD}}{X_{eD}}\right)\cos\left(\frac{m\pi X_D}{X_{eD}}\right)$$

$$\cdot \left[1 + e^{-\left(\frac{2\pi m Y_{eD}}{X_{eD}}\right)} + e^{-\left(\frac{2\pi m Y_{wD}}{X_{eD}}\right)} + e^{-\left(\frac{2\pi m(Y_{eD} - Y_{wD})}{X_{eD}}\right)}\right]\left[1 + \sum_{n=1}^{\infty}e^{-\frac{2mn\pi Y_{eD}}{X_{eD}}}\right]. \qquad (8.23)$$

For a vertical well intersected by a symmetric, finite-conductivity vertical fracture centrally located in the middle of a closed, cylindrical reservoir, the appropriate boundary-dominated flow image function is given by Eq. 8.24.

$$\xi = \ln\left(r_{eD}\right) + \frac{1}{4} + \sigma\left(X_D^{\,*},0\right) + \delta\left(X_D^{\,*},r_{eD}\right). \quad \dots\dots\dots\dots\dots\dots\dots\dots\dots\dots\dots \text{(8.24)}$$

The dimensionless drainage radius in this case (vertical fracture) is defined as the effective drainage radius of the well divided by the effective fracture half-length ($r_{eD}=r_e/L_c=r_e/X_f$).

The pseudoskin component caused by the finite-conductivity fracture (σ) can be determined with Eq. 8.25.

$$\sigma\left(X_D^{\,*},0\right) = 0.5\left[\left(X_D^{\,*}-1\right)\ln\left(1-X_D^{\,*}\right) - \left(X_D^{\,*}+1\right)\ln\left(1+X_D^{\,*}\right)\right]. \quad \dots\dots\dots\dots\dots\dots \text{(8.25)}$$

The equivalent dimensionless fracture spatial position $\left(X_D^{\,*}\right)$ used to accurately reproduce the wellbore rate or pressure-transient behavior of a finite-conductivity fracture (for $C_{fD} \geq 4.1635$) during the pseudoradial and boundary-dominated flow regime can be evaluated (Poe 2005) using Eq. 8.26.

$$X_D^{\,*} = 0.7355 - 1.5609\left(\frac{1}{C_{fD}}\right) + 1.5313\left(\frac{1}{C_{fD}}\right)^2 - 179.4346\left(\frac{1}{C_{fD}}\right)^3$$

$$+3928.97\left(\frac{1}{C_{fD}}\right)^4 - 40211.24\left(\frac{1}{C_{fD}}\right)^5$$

$$+183267.48\left(\frac{1}{C_{fD}}\right)^6 - 305367.26\left(\frac{1}{C_{fD}}\right)^7. \quad \dots\dots\dots\dots\dots\dots\dots\dots \text{(8.26)}$$

The dimensionless fracture conductivity is defined in the conventional manner shown in Eq. 8.27. The dimensionless fracture conductivity is a relative measure of the contrast of the fracture conductivity ($k_f b_f$) to the formation effective permeability (k) and the system characteristic length ($L_c=X_f$).

$$C_{fD} = \frac{k_f b_f}{kL_c} = \frac{k_f b_f}{kX_f}. \quad \dots\dots\dots\dots\dots\dots\dots\dots\dots\dots\dots\dots\dots\dots\dots\dots\dots \text{(8.27)}$$

Note: The equivalent fracture spatial position away from the well location at which to evaluate the uniform flux fracture solution to obtain the equivalent wellbore response as that of an infinite-conductivity vertical fracture ($X_D^{\,*}$) obtained with Eq. 8.26 is equal to 0.7355. This value is only slightly larger than the value commonly reported in the literature for evaluating an infinite-conductivity fracture response from the uniform flux solution (0.732), originally reported in Gringarten et al. (1974). The correlation presented in Eq. 8.26 (as well as the underlying values from which it was developed) are preferred for evaluating the finite-conductivity fracture response with the uniform flux solution. This also includes the evaluation of the infinite-conductivity fractured well response with the uniform flux solution.

The pseudoskin function caused by the bounded nature of the reservoir (δ) is defined (Ozkan 1988) with Eq. 8.28.

$$\delta\left(X_D^{\,*},r_{eD}\right) = \frac{\left[\left(X_D^{\,*}+1\right)^3 - \left(X_D^{\,*}-1\right)^3\right]}{12\,r_{eD}^{\,2}}. \quad \dots\dots\dots\dots\dots\dots\dots\dots\dots\dots\dots \text{(8.28)}$$

The image function that applies for a finite-conductivity vertically fractured well located in a closed, rectangular reservoir of dimensions X_{eD} by Y_{eD}, with the midpoint of the fracture located at (X_{wD}, Y_{wD}), is given (Poe 2002) by Eq. 8.29.

$$\xi = 2\pi\frac{Y_{eD}}{X_{eD}}\left(\frac{1}{3} - \frac{Y_D}{Y_{eD}} + \frac{Y_D^{\,2} + Y_{wD}^{\,2}}{2Y_{eD}^{\,2}}\right)$$

$$+ \frac{2X_{eD}}{\pi} \sum_{m=1}^{\infty} \frac{1}{m^2} \sin\left(\frac{m\pi}{X_{eD}}\right) \cos\left(\frac{m\pi X_{wD}}{X_{eD}}\right) \cos\left(\frac{m\pi X_D}{X_{eD}}\right)$$

$$\bullet \frac{\cosh\left[\dfrac{m\pi\left(Y_{eD} - |Y_D - Y_{wD}|\right)}{X_{eD}}\right] + \cosh\left[\dfrac{m\pi\left(Y_{eD} - (Y_D + Y_{wD})\right)}{X_{eD}}\right]}{\sinh\left(\dfrac{m\pi Y_{eD}}{X_{eD}}\right)}. \quad \dotfill \quad (8.29)$$

The solution for the image function of a vertically fractured well in a closed rectangle (Eq. 8.29) can also be recast into a more readily computable form for a wellbore spatial position of (X_{wD}, Y_{wD}), with a finite-conductivity fracture evaluation spatial location of $(X_D = X_{wD} + X_D^*, Y_D = Y_{wD})$, as given in Eq. 8.30.

$$\xi = 2\pi \frac{Y_{eD}}{X_{eD}}\left(\frac{1}{3} - \frac{Y_{wD}}{Y_{eD}} + \frac{Y_{wD}^2}{Y_{eD}^2}\right)$$

$$+ \frac{2X_{eD}}{\pi} \sum_{m=1}^{\infty} \frac{1}{m^2} \sin\left(\frac{m\pi}{X_{eD}}\right) \cos\left(\frac{m\pi X_{wD}}{X_{eD}}\right) \cos\left(\frac{m\pi X_D}{X_{eD}}\right)$$

$$\bullet \left[1 + e^{-\left(\frac{2\pi m Y_{eD}}{X_{eD}}\right)} + e^{-\left(\frac{2\pi m Y_{wD}}{X_{eD}}\right)} + e^{-\left(\frac{2\pi m (Y_{eD} - Y_{wD})}{X_{eD}}\right)}\right]\left[1 + \sum_{n=1}^{\infty} e^{\left(-\frac{2mn\pi Y_{eD}}{X_{eD}}\right)}\right]. \quad \dotfill \quad (8.30)$$

Similar expressions of the appropriate image functions can also be derived for horizontal wells located in closed circular or rectangular reservoirs (Ozkan 1988). For a uniform flux horizontal well with the midpoint of the effective wellbore length exposed to the reservoir centered in a closed, cylindrical reservoir, the appropriate image function is presented in a readily computable form with Eq. 8.31. The solution presented in Eq. 8.31 is expressed in terms of modified Bessel functions of the first kind of orders zero and one (I_0 and I_1) and the modified Bessel functions of the second kind of orders zero and one (K_0 and K_1), as well as integrals of the modified Bessel functions of the first and second kind of order zero.

$$\xi = \ln(r_{eD}) + \frac{1}{4} + \sigma(X_D, 0) + \delta(X_D, 0, r_{eD})$$

$$+ \frac{1}{\pi L_D} \sum_{n=1}^{\infty} \frac{\cos(n\pi Z_D) + \cos(n\pi Z_{wD})}{n}\left\{\int_0^{n\pi L_D(1+X_D)} K_0(u)\,du + \int_0^{n\pi L_D(1-X_D)} K_0(u)\,du\right.$$

$$+ \frac{K_1(n\pi L_D r_{eD})}{I_1(n\pi L_D r_{eD})}\left[\int_0^{n\pi L_D(1+X_D)} I_0(u)\,du + \int_0^{n\pi L_D(1-X_D)} I_0(u)\,du\right]\bigg\}. \quad \dotfill \quad (8.31)$$

Note: For a horizontal well centrally located in a cylindrical, bounded reservoir, the dimensionless drainage radius is defined as the ratio of the effective drainage radius of the circular reservoir divided by the system characteristic length, which in this case is equal to half the effective horizontal wellbore length in the pay zone ($r_{eD} = r_e/L_c = 2r_e/L_h$).

The imaging function for a uniform flux horizontal well located in a closed, rectangular reservoir can also be derived using the late-time solutions reported in Ozkan (1988). The late-time imaging function (ξ) for a horizontal well (with all its components), when expressed in a readily computable form, is quite lengthy but has been included in this discussion for completeness. The general solution is given by Eq. 8.32. Composite production decline curves for infinite-conductivity horizontal wells (uniform flux solution evaluated at $X_D = X_{wD} + 0.732$) (Gringarten et al. 1974) in closed, rectangular reservoirs have also been reported in Shih and

Blasingame (1995). The appropriate wellbore solution is evaluated at the reservoir spatial position $(X_D = X_{wD} + X_D^*, Y_D = Y_{wD}, Z_D = Z_{wD} + r_{wD})$, with $X_D^* = 0.732$.

$$\xi = \xi_f + P_{Db} + P_{Db1} + P_{Db2} + P_{Db3}. \quad \dotsfill (8.32)$$

The image function for an infinite-conductivity horizontal well located in a closed, rectangular reservoir (Eq. 8.32) can be evaluated as the sum of the corresponding image function of an infinite-conductivity vertical fracture in a closed, rectangular reservoir (ξ_f) given by Eq. 8.30 evaluated at $X_D = X_{wD} + X_D^* = X_{wD} + 0.732$, and with the remaining imaging components given in readily computable forms by Eqs. 8.33 through 8.36.

$$P_{Db} = \frac{1}{\pi L_D} \sum_{n=1}^{\infty} \frac{\cos(n\pi Z_D)\cos(n\pi Z_{wD})}{n}$$

$$\cdot \left[\int_0^{n\pi L_D(1+X_D-X_{wD})} K_0(u)\,du + \int_0^{n\pi L_D(1-X_D+X_{wD})} K_0(u)\,du \right]. \quad \dotsfill (8.33)$$

$$P_{Db1} = \frac{2}{X_{eD} L_D} \sum_{n=1}^{\infty} \frac{\cos(n\pi Z_D)\cos(n\pi Z_{wD})}{n} \left\{ \left[e^{-2n\pi L_D Y_{wD}} + e^{-2n\pi L_D Y_{eD}} \right. \right.$$

$$\left. + e^{-2n\pi L_D(Y_{eD}-Y_{wD})} \right] \left[1 + \sum_{m=1}^{\infty} e^{-2mn\pi L_D Y_{eD}} \right] + \sum_{m=1}^{\infty} e^{-2mn\pi L_D Y_{eD}} \right\}. \quad \dotsfill (8.34)$$

$$P_{Db2} = 4\sum_{m=1}^{\infty} \cos(m\pi Z_D)\cos(m\pi Z_{wD}) \sum_{n=1}^{\infty} \frac{\sin\left(\dfrac{n\pi}{X_{eD}}\right)\cos\left(\dfrac{n\pi X_D}{X_{eD}}\right)\cos\left(\dfrac{n\pi X_{wD}}{X_{eD}}\right)}{n\sqrt{m^2\pi^2 L_D^2 + \dfrac{n^2\pi^2}{X_{eD}^2}}}$$

$$\cdot \left\{ \left[e^{-2\sqrt{m^2\pi^2 L_D^2 + \frac{n^2\pi^2}{X_{eD}^2}}\,Y_{wD}} + e^{-2\sqrt{m^2\pi^2 L_D^2 + \frac{n^2\pi^2}{X_{eD}^2}}\,(Y_{eD}-Y_{wD})} + e^{-2\sqrt{m^2\pi^2 L_D^2 + \frac{n^2\pi^2}{X_{eD}^2}}\,Y_{eD}} \right] \right.$$

$$\cdot \left[1 + \sum_{j=1}^{\infty} e^{-2j\sqrt{m^2\pi^2 L_D^2 + \frac{n^2\pi^2}{X_{eD}^2}}\,Y_{eD}} \right] + \sum_{j=1}^{\infty} e^{-2j\sqrt{m^2\pi^2 L_D^2 + \frac{n^2\pi^2}{X_{eD}^2}}\,Y_{eD}} \right\} \quad \dotsfill (8.35)$$

$$P_{Db3} = \frac{1}{\pi L_D} \sum_{n=1}^{\infty} \frac{\cos(n\pi Z_D)\cos(n\pi Z_{wD})}{n}$$

$$\cdot \left\{ \int_0^{n\pi L_D(X_D+X_{wD}+1)} K_0(u)\,du - \int_0^{n\pi L_D(X_D+X_{wD}-1)} K_0(u)\,du \right.$$

$$+ \sum_{m=1}^{\infty} \left[\int_0^{n\pi L_D(2mX_{eD}-X_D+X_{wD}+1)} K_0(u)\,du - \int_0^{n\pi L_D(2mX_{eD}-X_D+X_{wD}-1)} K_0(u)\,du \right.$$

$$+ \int_0^{n\pi L_D(2mX_{eD}+X_D-X_{wD}+1)} K_0(u)\,du - \int_0^{n\pi L_D(2mX_{eD}+X_D-X_{wD}-1)} K_0(u)\,du$$

$$+ \int_0^{n\pi L_D \left(2mX_{eD} - X_D - X_{wD} + 1\right)} K_0\left(u\right) du - \int_0^{n\pi L_D \left(2mX_{eD} - X_D - X_{wD} - 1\right)} K_0\left(u\right) du$$

$$+ \int_0^{n\pi L_D \left(2mX_{eD} + X_D + X_{wD} + 1\right)} K_0\left(u\right) du - \int_0^{n\pi L_D \left(2mX_{eD} + X_D + X_{wD} - 1\right)} K_0\left(u\right) du \Bigg] \Bigg\}. \quad \dots\dots\dots\dots \quad (8.36)$$

Use of the dimensionless decline variables given by Eqs. 8.15, 8.16, and 8.18 and the corresponding scaling associated with each variable for both the transient and boundary-dominated flow behaviors of the production decline behavior of a well results in a composite reference decline curve set with only a single late-time stem for ease in graphical matching purposes.

8.4 Derivative and Integral Decline-Curve Analysis Functions

Another important and useful contribution of the production decline-curve analysis enhancements reported in Palacio and Blasingame (1993), Doublet and Blasingame (1995a, 1995b), Doublet et al. (1994), and Mc-Cray (1990) is the introduction and use of additional production decline response functions to aid in graphical matching of the historical production performance to reference production decline curves. The two response functions introduced and used to improve the uniqueness of the graphical matching procedure are the dimensionless decline flow rate integral and rate integral-derivative functions.

The dimensionless decline flow rate integral function is equivalent to the dimensionless decline cumulative-production function (Eq. 8.18) normalized by the dimensionless decline time (Eq. 8.16). The dimensionless flow rate integral-derivative is equal to the derivative of the dimensionless flow rate integral with respect to the natural logarithm of the dimensionless decline time function. These graphical analysis relationships tend to trend in the same general manner as the dimensionless decline flow rate function with respect to the dimensionless decline time and can provide a clearer demarcation of the flow regimes exhibited in the decline behavior of production performance of a well.

8.4.1 Fundamental Relationships. The dimensionless flow rate integral function introduced to aid in graphical production decline-curve analysis matching procedures is equal to the dimensionless decline time normalized dimensionless decline cumulative-production function. This function is significantly smoother than the dimensionless decline flow rate function (Eq. 8.14), yet even though it is smoother than the decline flow rate function, it does not suffer any appreciable loss in character of the production decline trend for a particular flow regime. This relationship is expressed mathematically in Eq. 8.37, which is applicable for all values of dimensionless decline time, or with Eq. 8.38, which is only applicable for boundary-dominated flow.

$$q_{Ddi}\left(t_{Dd}\right) = \frac{1}{t_{Dd}} \int_0^{t_{Dd}} q_{Dd}\left(\tau\right) d\tau = \frac{Q_{pDd}\left(t_{Dd}\right)}{t_{Dd}} \quad \left\{\text{all values of } t_{Dd}\right\}. \quad \dots\dots\dots\dots \quad (8.37)$$

$$q_{Ddi}\left(t_{Dd}\right) = \frac{1}{t_{Dd}}\left[1 - q_{Dd}\left(t_{Dd}\right)\right] \quad \left\{\text{boundary-dominated flow only}\right\}. \quad \dots\dots\dots\dots \quad (8.38)$$

The derivative of the dimensionless flow rate integral function with respect to the natural logarithm of the dimensionless decline time function has also been used to provide a more distinctive character of the transient-production decline behavior than either the dimensionless decline flow rate or flow rate integral functions. The enhanced signature characteristic of the dimensionless decline flow rate integral-derivative function makes it extremely useful for identifying the start and end of a particular flow regime, as well as for improving the uniqueness of the decline-curve analysis graphical matching procedure. This relationship is stated in Eqs. 8.39 and 8.40. Note: Eq. 8.39 is applicable for all values of t_{Dd}, while Eq. 8.40 applies only for boundary-dominated flow.

$$q_{Ddid}\left(t_{Dd}\right) = -\frac{dq_{Ddi}\left(t_{Dd}\right)}{d\ln\left(t_{Dd}\right)} = -t_{Dd}\frac{dq_{Ddi}\left(t_{Dd}\right)}{dt_{Dd}} = q_{Ddi}\left(t_{Dd}\right) - q_{Dd}\left(t_{Dd}\right). \quad \dots\dots\dots\dots \quad (8.39)$$

$$q_{Ddid}\left(t_{Dd}\right) = \frac{1}{t_{Dd}}\left[1 - q_{Dd}\left(t_{Dd}\right)\left[1 + t_{Dd}\right]\right] \quad \left\{\text{boundary-dominated flow}\right\}. \quad \dots\dots\dots\dots \quad (8.40)$$

8.4.2 Calculation Procedure for Plotting Functions. The analysis of the historical production decline data of a well using the dimensionless production decline solutions developed that are expressed in terms of the dimensionless decline variables of flow rate, flow rate integral, and flow rate integral-derivative requires that the appropriate dimensional production decline functions be computed directly from the historical production data. The dimensional graphical analysis variables derived from the historical production data used are the pressure drawdown normalized flow rate, pressure drawdown normalized flow rate integral, and pressure drawdown normalized flow rate integral-derivative functions.

The appropriate graphical analysis dimensional variable that corresponds to the dimensionless decline flow rate function is the pressure drawdown normalized flow rate at each production data time level. This graphical analysis function is computed directly from the historical production data, as indicated in Eq. 8.41. Note: The pressure drawdown used to normalize the dimensional graphical analysis variables is referenced to the initial reservoir pore pressure, p_i.

$$\frac{q}{\Delta p}(t) = \frac{q(t)}{p_i - p_{wf}(t)}. \dots\dots\dots\dots\dots\dots\dots\dots (8.41)$$

The dimensional pressure drawdown normalized flow rate integral function in a graphical analysis corresponds to the dimensionless flow rate integral function response of the system. This variable is evaluated as an integration of the dimensional pressure drawdown normalized flow rate history with respect to the material balance time and normalized with the material balance time function. The evaluation of this variable requires the use of an accurate and efficient numerical integration technique.

Doublet and Blasingame (1995a) recommended that the trapezoidal rule of integration be used for this purpose. However, the Gauss Quadrature has been found to be equally well or better suited for this function evaluation. Whichever numerical integration technique is used, it is important to include the capability of an extrapolation of the pressure drawdown normalized flow rate function to time-zero ($t=0$) for the proper integration of the pressure drawdown normalized flow rate integral function. The mathematical definition of this dimensional graphical analysis function is given in Eq. 8.42.

$$\left[\frac{q}{\Delta p}\right]_i(t) = \frac{1}{t_{mb}(t)}\int_0^{t_{mb}(t)}\frac{q}{\Delta p}(\tau)d\tau = \frac{1}{t_{mb}(t)}\int_0^{t_{mb}(t)}\frac{q(\tau)}{p_i - p_{wf}(\tau)}d\tau. \dots\dots\dots (8.42)$$

The dimensional graphical analysis variable that corresponds to the production decline response of the dimensionless flow rate integral-derivative function is the pressure drawdown normalized flow rate integral-derivative function. This dimensional graphical analysis derivative function is defined mathematically in Eq. 8.43 and is computed as the first derivative of the pressure drawdown normalized flow rate integral function with respect to the natural logarithm of the material balance time.

$$\left[\frac{q}{\Delta p}\right]_{id}(t) = -\frac{d\left[\left[\frac{q}{\Delta p}\right]_i(t)\right]}{d\ln(t_{mb}(t))} = -t_{mb}(t)\frac{d\left[\left[\frac{q}{\Delta p}\right]_i(t)\right]}{dt_{mb}(t)}. \dots\dots\dots\dots\dots\dots (8.43)$$

8.5 Production Decline Response of an Unfractured Well in a Closed Reservoir

Using the dimensionless decline flow rate, flow rate integral, and flow rate integral-derivative functions previously defined, reference production decline sets can be readily constructed for use in a graphical analysis of the production decline behavior of a well. All that is required to construct the necessary dimensionless production decline curves is an appropriate rate-transient solution for the well and reservoir type of interest.

For example, the rate-transient response of an unfractured vertical well in a closed, cylindrical reservoir can be readily computed as a function of dimensionless time using the finite wellbore Laplace space pressure-transient solution for this problem given by van Everdingen and Hurst (1949). The real space solution can then be readily computed by evaluating the Laplace space dimensionless wellbore flow rate solution by application of Duhamel's theorem (Faltung principle) with the Laplace space pressure-transient solution and using a numerical Laplace transform inversion algorithm, such as the one reported by Stehfest (1970). The dimensionless decline variable transforms given by Eqs. 8.15, 8.16, 8.37, and 8.39 can then be used to generate the required reference production decline-curve set.

Two general types of production decline-curve solution presentations have been used for decline-curve analyses. The more popular of these is a log-log graph of the dimensionless decline flow rate (and possibly the decline flow rate integral and flow rate integral-derivative functions) vs. the dimensionless decline time (q_{Dd} vs. t_{Dd}). An alternative presentation of the dimensionless production decline response occasionally used for production decline analyses is a log-log graph of the same ordinate axis decline flow rate variables (q_{Dd}, q_{Ddi}, and q_{Ddid}) as a function of the dimensionless decline cumulative production (Q_{pDd}).

A graphical presentation of the reference production decline curves for an unfractured vertical well centrally located in a closed, cylindrical reservoir, presented in the more conventional manner (q_{Dd} vs. t_{Dd}), is given in **Fig. 8.4.** In Fig. 8.4, the dimensionless decline flow rate response is presented as black curves, the dimensionless flow rate integral behavior is given by red curves, and the derivative response is presented in blue. Only the derivative function curves are labeled in Fig. 8.4 for the dimensionless drainage radius values of 10 to 1,000 to improve clarity by reducing the number of curve labels presented. However, the correspondence of the curves during the transient flow regime can be readily discerned because the uppermost decline flow rate integral curve (r_{eD}=10) corresponds to the uppermost decline flow rate curve, as well as corresponding to the uppermost derivative curve. There is a one-to-one correspondence of these functions during the transient flow regime.

Note: In Fig. 8.4, the dimensionless decline flow rate integral and flow rate integral-derivative functions have a negative unity slope during the boundary-dominated flow regime, while the dimensionless decline flow rate function has an exponential decline behavior, as defined from the specific analytic solutions for those functions given in Eqs. 8.38, 8.40, and 8.14, respectively. Therefore, from a fundamental basis that adheres rigorously to rate-transient fluid flow theory, a mathematical justification for a harmonic production decline (Doublet and Blasingame 1995a) during boundary-dominated flow, without first assuming that a steady-state relationship exists between the pressure-transient and rate-transient solutions at late time, is unwarranted for theoretical purists at heart. However, as has been observed in practice for a very long time, we do see late-time production decline trends that do deviate (i.e., sometimes significantly) from the exponential decline behavior and can tend to exhibit a harmonic decline behavior. This deviation from the theoretical decline behavior may be caused by a number of factors, including the effects of nonlinear fluid and reservoir properties, reservoir layering and other heterogeneity effects, and external boundary pressure support. If the latter factor is present in the system, then steady-state conditions may actually exist, and a harmonic production decline may be observed.

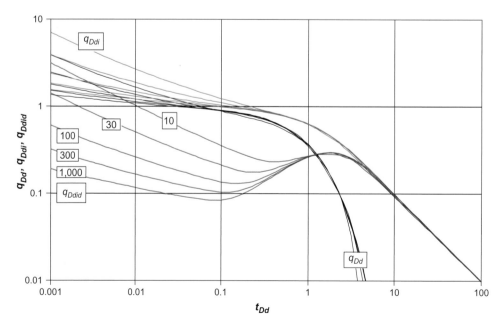

Fig. 8.4—Production decline curves for an unfractured vertical well centrally located in a closed, cylindrical reservoir.

Note: Also in Fig. 8.4, the dimensionless decline flow rate integral-derivative function has more vertical separation on the ordinate axis than do the dimensionless decline flow rate and flow rate integral functions during the transient flow regime. This fact permits the use of the decline flow rate integral-derivative function response as a means of obtaining improved accuracy in the determination of the dimensionless drainage radius (i.e., decline stem parameter) in a graphical decline analysis matching procedure.

Problem. At a dimensionless decline time function value of 0.01, the dimensionless decline flow rate function for an unfractured vertical well in a closed, cylindrical reservoir has a value of 0.88 and a flow rate integral value of 1.07. What is the dimensionless decline flow rate integral-derivative value that corresponds to this value of dimensionless decline time? What is the dimensionless drainage radius of the well?

Solution. Because the dimensionless decline time value falls in the transient flow regime (Fig. 8.4), the dimensionless decline flow rate integral-derivative function value can be directly evaluated using Eq. 8.39.

$$q_{Ddid}\left(t_{Dd}\right) = q_{Ddi}\left(t_{Dd}\right) - q_{Dd}\left(t_{Dd}\right) = 1.07 - 0.88 = 0.19 .$$

From Fig. 8.4, at a dimensionless decline time of 0.01, the decline stem with a derivative value in closest agreement with this value is the one with a dimensionless drainage radius of 100.

8.6 Decline-Curve Analyses for Other Types of Wells
Reference production decline curves can be constructed for a wide variety of well types and outer-boundary conditions using the general methodology proposed by Doublet and Blasingame (1995a). For example, there have been reference production decline curve sets developed for vertically fractured and infinite-conductivity horizontal wells (Shih and Blasingame 1995) in closed, rectangular reservoirs. Various external-boundary flux models have also been developed for unfractured vertical wells (Doublet and Blasingame 1995b) using this general decline-curve construction methodology. The latter case is particularly interesting, because it demonstrates that the decline-curve development technique proposed by Doublet and Blasingame (1995a) could be extended to reservoirs with outer boundaries not entirely closed. In this particular case, the methodology was used to develop reference decline-curve sets to consider water encroachment caused by water influx or waterflood operations.

8.6.1 Solutions for Other Outer-Boundary Conditions. Two types of single-phase flow boundary flux models were proposed by Doublet and Blasingame (1995b) for an unfractured vertical well centered in a cylindrical,, bounded reservoir. These are the step-rate and ramp-rate boundary flux models. The influx at the outer boundary is initially equal to zero (no-flow outer-boundary condition), which permits the use of the closed-boundary rate-transient decline curve analysis development procedure previously discussed, at least for the limiting case of a no influx outer-boundary condition. While the nonzero boundary flux conditions do not result in the exponential production decline behavior given by Eq. 8.14, the no-influx limiting case does, and the nonzero influx cases can be considered as deviations from this decline behavior.

The corrected form of the Laplace transform boundary flux pressure-transient solution (Doublet and Blasingame (1995b) is included in this text with Eq. 8.44. The Laplace transform solution is expressed in terms of the modified Bessel function of the first and second kinds, of orders zero and one. The Laplace space transform parameter (s) corresponds to the dimensionless time values at which to evaluate the solution.

Note: For the special case of no-influx [$q_{Dext}(s)=0$], the solution given in Eq. 8.44 reduces to the result obtained by van Everdingen and Hurst (1949) for a volumetric reservoir. The corresponding Laplace transform solutions of the no-flow, step-rate, and ramp-rate boundary flux conditions are given in Eq. 8.45. At a specific point in time (t_{Dstart}) in the production history, the outer-boundary condition is switched from the initial no-flow condition to a specified flux condition (q_{Dext}), according to one of the influx models given in Eq. 8.45.

$$\tilde{p}_{wD}(s) = \frac{K_0\left(\sqrt{s}\right)I_1\left(\sqrt{s}r_{eD}\right) + I_0\left(\sqrt{s}\right)K_1\left(\sqrt{s}r_{eD}\right)}{s\sqrt{s}\left[K_1\left(\sqrt{s}\right)I_1\left(\sqrt{s}r_{eD}\right) - I_1\left(\sqrt{s}\right)K_1\left(\sqrt{s}r_{eD}\right)\right]}$$

$$+ \frac{\tilde{q}_{Dext}(s)}{\sqrt{s}r_{eD}}\frac{\left[K_0\left(\sqrt{s}\right)I_1\left(\sqrt{s}\right) + I_0\left(\sqrt{s}\right)K_1\left(\sqrt{s}\right)\right]}{\left[K_1\left(\sqrt{s}\right)I_1\left(\sqrt{s}r_{eD}\right) - I_1\left(\sqrt{s}\right)K_1\left(\sqrt{s}r_{eD}\right)\right]} . \quad \dots \dots \quad (8.44)$$

$$\tilde{q}_{Dext}(s) = \begin{cases} 0, & \text{no-flow} \\ -\dfrac{1}{s}q_{Dext\infty}\exp(-t_{Dstart}s), & \text{step-rate} \\ \dfrac{-q_{Dext\infty}}{s(1+t_{Dstart}\,s)}, & \text{ramp-rate} \end{cases} \quad \dots \dots \dots \dots \dots (8.45)$$

As discussed previously, the real space rate-transient solution of the boundary flux model can be readily obtained by evaluation of the Laplace space dimensionless wellbore flow rate solution obtained by application of Duhamel's theorem (Eq. 8.46) and then numerically inverting the result into the real space domain (Stehfest 1970).

$$\tilde{q}_{wD}(s) = \frac{1}{s^2 \tilde{p}_{wD}(s)} \cdot \quad \dots \dots \dots \dots \dots \dots \dots \dots \dots \dots \dots \dots \dots \dots (8.46)$$

The step-rate boundary flux model assumes that the outer-boundary condition is abruptly switched to a specified flux condition at a prescribed point in time, and the influx rate is held constant thereafter. This decline analysis model was developed to address issues related to waterflood operations. The production decline behavior obtained with the model exhibits production "humps" similar to those commonly observed in producing wells in waterflooded fields.

The reference decline-curve set generated with the step-rate boundary flux model is presented in **Fig. 8.5.** The range of dimensionless drainage radius values depicted in this figure is from 5 to 1,000; the boundary flux values range from 0 to 1; and the dimensionless time at which the influx starts ranges from 0.1 to 30. Note: For a value of (q_{Dext}) of 0, the volumetric reservoir behavior is obtained; and for a (q_{Dext}) value of 1, steady-state flow conditions exist.

The ramp-rate boundary flux model assumes that the outer-boundary condition (initially at zero influx) smoothly and slowly increases from time-zero to a fixed larger value at a later time. This decline analysis model was developed to approximate the production decline behaviors of reservoirs with natural water influx or slowly responding waterflood systems. The production decline behavior obtained with the ramp-rate boundary flux model is often found to be virtually indistinguishable from the production decline behavior of a dual-porosity reservoir.

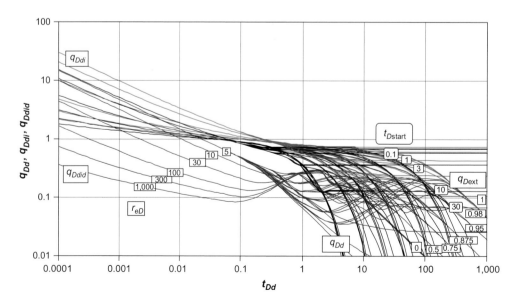

Fig. 8.5—Production decline curves for an unfractured vertical well centrally located in a cylindrical reservoir with a step-rate flux outer-boundary condition.

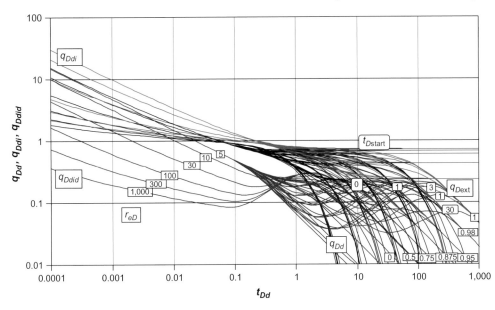

Fig. 8.6—Production decline curves for an unfractured vertical well centrally located in a cylindrical reservoir with a ramp-rate flux outer-boundary condition.

The reference decline-curve set generated with the ramp-rate boundary flux model is presented in **Fig. 8.6.** The same ranges of dimensionless variable values (r_{eD}, q_{Dext}, and t_{Dstart}) are considered in this illustration as were used in Fig. 8.5 for the step-rate boundary flux model.

Multiphase numerical reservoir simulation runs were made in the Doublet and Blasingame (1995b) investigation to validate the use of the single-phase analysis step-rate and ramp-rate boundary flux models for the production decline analysis of two-phase systems, in which water displaced oil. It was reported that the single-phase model developed in Doublet and Blasingame (1995b) should be applicable for oil/water two-phase systems with mobility ratios near unity, potentially being applicable to an injection-production system analogous to that of a five- or nine-spot pattern.

8.6.2 Vertically Fractured Well-Injection Decline Analysis. Application of the recent developments in decline-curve model construction was also made to the development of production/injection decline curves for infinite-conductivity vertically fractured wells located in closed, cylindrical reservoirs (Doublet and Blasingame 1995a). The uniform flux fracture solution of Ozkan (1988) was used in that study to rapidly (and with reasonable accuracy) estimate the infinite-conductivity fractured well response at a dimensionless fracture spatial position from the wellbore equal to 0.732 (Gringarten et al. 1974).

The reference decline-curve set generated using this solution is presented in **Fig. 8.7** for a range of dimensionless drainage radius ($r_{eD}=r_e/X_f$) values of 1 to 1,000. Once again, only the derivative function curves are labeled, but the same correspondence between the decline flow rate, flow rate integral, and flow rate integral-derivative functions are observed. The uppermost decline flow rate integral curve ($r_{eD}=1$) during the infinite-acting transient behavior corresponds to the uppermost decline flow rate and derivative curves.

A generally more appropriate production reference decline-curve set can be constructed for an infinite-conductivity vertical fracture in a closed, rectangular reservoir using the uniform flux solution developed by Ozkan (1988). It was reported in the literature by a number of investigators that the reservoir area effectively drained (or over which the pressure distribution was influenced) by a vertically fractured well in a low-permeability reservoir is directly a function of the effective fracture half-length. This results in a drained area in the reservoir typically more elliptical in shape during the transient flow regimes. An elongated rectangular drainage area is therefore generally considered to be more appropriate than a circular drainage area when modeling the transient behavior of vertically fractured wells in finite reservoirs. Because the infinite-conductivity fracture is simply a special case of the finite-conductivity ($C_{fD}>500$) fractured well in a closed, rectangular

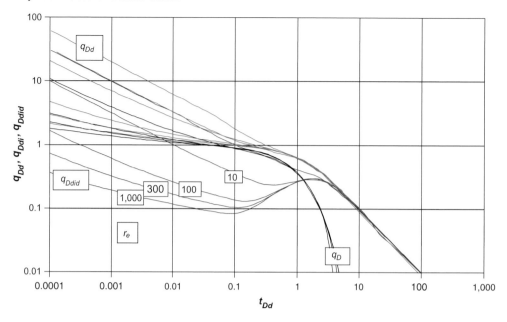

Fig. 8.7—Production decline curves for an infinite-conductivity fractured well centrally located in a closed, cylindrical reservoir.

reservoir, this limiting case can therefore be readily included in the reference decline-curve sets for a finite-conductivity vertical fracture in a rectangular reservoir.

8.6.3 Vertical Wells Intersected by Finite-Conductivity Fractures. Production decline curves for finite-conductivity vertically fractured wells can also be constructed using the methodology reported in Doublet and Blasingame (1995a). The image function for coupling the transient and boundary-dominated flow decline stems is given by Eq. 8.24 for a vertically fractured well centrally located in a closed, cylindrical reservoir and by Eq. 8.29 for a vertically fractured well located in a closed, rectangular reservoir. The pseudoskin functions required for computing the image function of a vertically fractured well in a closed, cylindrical reservoir are given by Eqs. 8.25 and 8.28, for the pseudoskin components caused by the finite-conductivity of the fracture and the effects of the boundary, respectively. The conventional definition of the dimensionless fracture conductivity is given in Eq. 8.27, and the corresponding dimensionless fracture spatial position away from the wellbore (i.e., center of a symmetric bi-wing fracture) at which to evaluate the uniform flux solution to generate the finite-conductivity fracture response is given by Eq. 8.26.

With the finite-conductivity vertical-fracture solution, a graphical depiction of a single comprehensive set of production decline curves that incorporates all of the independent variables in a 2D graphical solution is impractical. With typical dimensionless production decline curves, it is practical to display the dimensionless production decline response functions (q_{Dd}, q_{Ddi}, and q_{Ddid}) in terms of at most two independent variables. These are typically in terms of the dimensionless decline time or cumulative production and a single parameter, such as the dimensionless drainage radius (or area) as a parameter of each of the transient production decline stems. The exceptions to this rule are of course the boundary flux solutions given in Figs. 8.5 and 8.6. It was possible to display a complete set of production decline curves for the boundary flux solution in a single comprehensive production decline curve suite because the effects of the boundary flux are exhibited only during the boundary-dominated flow regime, and the effect of dimensionless drainage radius is the governing parameter of the transient production decline behavior. Even then, as one can readily see in the late-time behavior of those figures, the result is often a confusing mass of curves that make graphical matching procedures quite difficult.

However, with the finite-conductivity vertical-fracture solution (or the infinite-conductivity horizontal-well solution that follows), there are three or more parameters that govern the transient production decline behavior of the well. In the case of a finite-conductivity vertical fracture centrally located in a closed, cylindrical reservoir, the transient production decline stems of the coupled transient and boundary-dominated flow be-

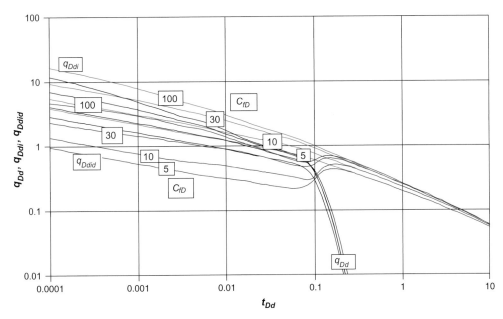

Fig. 8.8—Production decline curves for a finite-conductivity vertically fractured well centrally located in a closed, 2 × 1 rectangle reservoir, $AD = 8$.

haviors are functions of the dimensionless drainage radius and the dimensionless fracture conductivity, in addition to being a function of the dimensionless decline time.

Similarly, a finite-conductivity vertical fracture in a closed, rectangular reservoir has transient dimensionless decline stems that are a function of the dimensionless fracture conductivity, the dimensionless drainage area, the dimensionless spatial position of the well in the drainage area, and the dimensionless decline time. Therefore, it is generally required that a family of reference dimensionless decline curve sets be developed for each of these cases, with each composite reference decline curve set developed for fixed values of one or more of the independent variables of the problem.

An example of a dimensionless production decline-curve set for a finite-conductivity fracture is given in **Fig. 8.8.** This decline-curve set was developed for a fractured well centrally located in a 2 × 1 rectangle with a dimensionless drainage area of 8. A complete family of reference production decline curves for a finite-conductivity fractured well includes other decline-curve sets for a range of dimensionless fracture conductivity and drainage area and/or aspect ratio.

8.6.4 Infinite-Conductivity Horizontal Wellbore. Dimensionless production decline curves for an infinite-conductivity horizontal wellbore also have three or more independent parameters that govern their transient dimensionless production decline behavior. For an infinite-conductivity horizontal wellbore centrally located in a closed, circular reservoir, the required image function for coupling the transient and boundary-dominated flow production decline behaviors is given in Eq. 8.31. The independent variables that govern the transient behavior of the well in this case are the dimensionless wellbore length ($L_D=L_h/2h$), the dimensionless drainage radius ($r_{eD}=r_e/L_c=2r_e/L_h$), the dimensionless wellbore radius ($r_{wD}=r_w/h$), the dimensionless wellbore vertical spatial position (or standoff from the bottom) in the reservoir, and the dimensionless decline time.

The production decline behavior of an infinite-conductivity horizontal well located in a closed, rectangular reservoir is even more complex. The transient production decline behavior of an infinite-conductivity horizontal well located in a closed rectangle is a function of the dimensionless wellbore length, the dimensionless wellbore radius, the standoff from the bottom of the reservoir, the reservoir drainage area, the wellbore midpoint location in the drainage area, and the dimensionless decline time. This list of parameters is the minimum that must be considered. Additionally, the effects of reservoir permeability anisotropy and dual-porosity behavior may also be included in the family of reference production decline curves, even further expanding the number of reference curve sets required.

Examples of production decline-curve sets for an infinite-conductivity horizontal well located in a closed, rectangular drainage area can be found in Shih and Blasingame (1995). Even though the original manuscript was not complete when presented, a reasonably extensive set of production decline curves for an infinite-conductivity horizontal well located in a closed, rectangular reservoir was presented. Shih and Blasingame noted that an improved coupling of the transient and boundary-dominated flow regime production decline stems was achieved by an empirical adjustment of the image function by 0.1 ($\xi = \xi + 0.1$).

Theoretically, an empirical adjustment of the image function is not necessary. The convergence of the boundary-dominated flow decline stems to a single (i.e., exponential) decline stem using the unadjusted image function found to be satisfactory when sufficiently small convergence tolerances were used in the evaluation of the Fourier series of the image function. However, if the empirical adjustment to the image function recommended by Shih and Blasingame (1995) is made, this adjusted parameter must be used throughout all the decline analysis computations, both in the generation of the reference curve sets and in the dimensional decline analysis computations.

Problem. A vertically fractured well is centrally located in a closed, cylindrical reservoir with a dimensionless drainage area of 10. The fracture dimensionless conductivity is equal to 10. Determine the image function value required to generate the reference decline curve for these parameter values.

Solution. The equivalent fracture spatial position at which to evaluate the uniform flux fracture solution to obtain the finite-conductivity fracture response is determined using Eq. 8.26.

$$X_D^* = 0.7355 - 1.5609\left(\frac{1}{C_{fD}}\right) + 1.5313\left(\frac{1}{C_{fD}}\right)^2 - 179.4346\left(\frac{1}{C_{fD}}\right)^3$$

$$+ 3928.97\left(\frac{1}{C_{fD}}\right)^4 - 40211.24\left(\frac{1}{C_{fD}}\right)^5$$

$$+ 183267.48\left(\frac{1}{C_{fD}}\right)^6 - 305367.26\left(\frac{1}{C_{fD}}\right)^7.$$

$$X_D^* = 0.7355 - 1.5609\left(\frac{1}{10}\right) + 1.5313\left(\frac{1}{10}\right)^2 - 179.4346\left(\frac{1}{10}\right)^3$$

$$+ 3928.97\left(\frac{1}{10}\right)^4 - 40211.24\left(\frac{1}{10}\right)^5$$

$$+ 183267.48\left(\frac{1}{10}\right)^6 - 305367.26\left(\frac{1}{10}\right)^7 = 0.5588.$$

The pseudoskin effect caused by the finite-conductivity fracture is determined with Eq. 8.25.

$$\sigma\left(X_D^*,0\right) = 0.5\left[\left(X_D^* - 1\right)\ln\left(1 - X_D^*\right) - \left(X_D^* + 1\right)\ln\left(1 + X_D^*\right)\right]$$

$$\sigma\left(0.5588,0\right) = 0.5\left[\left(0.5588 - 1\right)\ln\left(1 - 0.5588\right) - \left(0.5588 + 1\right)\ln\left(1 + 0.5588\right)\right]$$

$$\sigma\left(0.5588,0\right) = -0.1655.$$

The dimensionless drainage radius is evaluated from the definition of the dimensionless drainage area of a circular drainage area.

$$r_{eD} = \sqrt{\frac{A_D}{\pi}} = \sqrt{\frac{10}{\pi}} = 1.7841.$$

The pseudoskin effect caused by the bounded nature of the reservoir is obtained using Eq. 8.28.

$$\delta\left(X_D^*, r_{eD}\right) = \frac{\left[\left(X_D^* + 1\right)^3 - \left(X_D^* - 1\right)^3\right]}{12\ r_{eD}^2}$$

$$\delta\left(0.5588, r_{eD}\right) = \frac{\left[\left(0.5588 + 1\right)^3 - \left(0.5588 - 1\right)^3\right]}{12\ (1.7841)^2} = 0.1014\ .$$

The image function value used to correlate this reference decline curve is given by Eq. 8.24.

$$\xi = \ln\left(r_{eD}\right) + \frac{1}{4} + \sigma\left(X_D^*, 0\right) + \delta\left(X_D^*, r_{eD}\right)$$

$$\xi = \ln\left(1.7841\right) + \frac{1}{4} - 0.1655 + 0.1014 = 0.7648\ .$$

8.7 Production Decline-Curve Analysis With Partial or Absent Pressure Record

A problem commonly encountered in the evaluation of the production performance of a well is one in which not all the required production data are available for analysis. This problem arises quite frequently and may result from a number of reasons. Whether performing a production decline-curve analysis using the material balance time approach, or a history match of the well performance data using a numerical model that uses superposition of the varying flow rate and flowing pressure history, the flow rates of each of the fluid phases as well as the bottomhole-flowing pressure are required at each time level in the production history to correctly perform the analysis.

If wellhead-flowing pressures are recorded, these values can be used in conjunction with the wellhead flow rate history and one of a number of industry-accepted wellbore pressure traverse models to estimate the bottomhole-flowing pressures that correspond to the wellhead-flowing pressure history. However, when some or all of the wellhead-flowing pressures or BHFPs are unavailable, the practicing engineer has only two options available for trying to estimate the missing bottomhole pressures to use in a production analysis that have an engineering basis. The simplest approach, though not necessarily the most correct, is to interpolate across the known wellhead-flowing pressures or BHFPs to try and fill in the missing values. This technique does not account for any inter- or intraday (or month, if monthly data) variation in the wellhead-flowing pressures or BHFPs and may be considered as only a crude approximation at best.

An alternate approach reported in the literature (Poe 2002, 2003, 2005; Poe and Marhaendrajana 2002) is one in which a hybrid of the corrected material balance time function and conventional superposition may be used to effectively perform a convolution analysis of the production performance of a well with an incomplete production data record. With this approach, the corrected material balance time function (i.e., equivalent of the superposition time) is used to fill in the missing equivalent time function values. From a decline-curve analysis match, the missing BHFPs can then be estimated from the matched decline-curve solution.

Another type of production data also often unavailable for consideration in an analysis of the production performance of a well is the water production, which is often inaccurately or sporadically recorded, or even commonly allocated if connected to a multiwell production system. The liquid voidage from the reservoir, whether it is produced water or hydrocarbon liquid, has a significant impact on the average reservoir pressure decline with production time. Gas produced from the well not properly accounted for can also have a significant effect on the accuracy of a production decline analysis. The issue of missing flow rate values in a production performance analysis is not readily addressed. However, analysis techniques have been developed for addressing the issue of missing BHFPs in the production data record that can make a valid production decline analysis possible.

8.7.1 Hybrid Equivalent Convolution Analysis. The use of a corrected material balance time equivalent of the superposition time for production time values for which the BHFPs are unavailable has a theoretical basis in rate-transient theory. The fundamental relationship between the material balance time function and superposition time (using the rate-transient approach) is expressed in Eqs. 8.7 through 8.9. A hybrid convolution technique of production decline analysis can be constructed that uses a conventional superposition-in-time formulation for all production time levels that have both the flow rates and the corresponding bottomhole-pressure data available, and an equivalent of the superposition time function values derived from a corrected material balance time function for data points with missing BHFPs. This hybrid convolution technique can be used to effectively evaluate the production performance of a well with incomplete production data records in a systematic and valid manner.

While it is always preferable to have all the production data values (e.g., flow rates and BHFPs) available for a production performance analysis so that conventional superposition analysis techniques can be used, at times this is not possible. The flow rate production data records can be used to directly calculate the material balance time not corrected. Depending on the well and reservoir type under consideration, the appropriate material balance time function correction can be determined from solution of the rate-transient behavior. Examples of the correction of the material balance time as a function of the superposition equivalent time are given in Figs. 8.1, 8.2, and 8.3 for finite-conductivity fractures, unfractured vertical wells, and infinite-conductivity horizontal wells, respectively.

8.7.2 Assumptions and Limitations. The effective convolution analysis technique previously described in this chapter is subject to limitations and assumptions. One of the limitations of the technique related to the use of the Horner approximation of the pseudoproducing time (e.g., material balance time) is that it is assumed that the flow rate is only permitted to be smoothly varying. Therefore, an erratic well flow history shortly before a production data time level of interest can result in a significant error in the estimation of the equivalent superposition time function value for that time level. This limitation is also true for other production analysis methods that use the material balance time function as a substitute for the superposition time function.

A limitation of the graphical analysis technique associated with the hybrid convolution methodology is that because it is part of a graphical decline curve analysis technique, uniqueness issues may often arise. This is particularly true in this case, because the graphical decline-curve analyses associated with this production decline analysis methodology are dimensionless flow rate vs. cumulative production decline-curve sets. In addition to being very similar in shape to one another, these decline-curve sets also tend to be more compressed in scale in the transient and boundary-dominated flow regimes than the conventional decline flow rate vs. time graphical analyses, in effect making the decline matching procedure more prone to uniqueness and accuracy issues.

Problem. During the formation linear flow regime, an infinite-conductivity (or finite-conductivity with $C_{fD}>500$) fractured well has a material balance time function value that is two times that of the corresponding superposition time (Fig. 8.1). Similarly, during the bilinear flow regime of a finite-conductivity vertical fracture, the dimensionless material balance time has a value that is 4/3 that of the superposition time. Note: Both values can be identified at a dimensionless time of approximately 1×10^{-4} or earlier in Fig. 8.1 for the two flow regimes of different dimensionless conductivity fractures. The relationship between the two time functions for a dimensionless fracture conductivity of 100 exhibits a maximum during the pseudolinear flow regime of approximately 1.875 at a dimensionless superposition time of approximately 1.1×10^{-2}. Considering the example finite-conductivity fractured well production decline behavior given in Fig. 8.8 for a 2 × 1 rectangle with a dimensionless drainage area of 8, the image function value used to scale the production decline curves for a C_{fD} value of 100 is essentially equal to 0.2618. Note: In Eq. 8.29, the dimensionless fracture conductivity has only a minor effect and is included in the spatial position $(X_D=X_{wD}+X_D^*)$ at which the solution is evaluated. What is the maximum effect on the production decline time, flow rate, and flow rate integral values at which the solution is matched for a fracture with a dimensionless conductivity of 100 during the pseudolinear flow regime?

Solution. The dimensionless time referenced to the drainage area is evaluated using Eq. 8.12.

$$t_{DA}(t) = \frac{t_D(t)}{A_D} = \frac{10^{-2}}{8} = 1.25 \times 10^{-3}.$$

The dimensionless decline time that truly reflects the superposition time is computed using Eq. 8.16.

$$t_{Dd} = \frac{2\pi}{\xi} t_{DA} = \frac{2\pi}{0.2618}\left(1.25 \times 10^{-3}\right) = 3 \times 10^{-2}.$$

From Fig. 8.8, the dimensionless decline flow rate at this decline time value is equal to 0.959, and the flow rate integral is equal to 1.78. The apparent decline time obtained if the uncorrected material balance time function were used is therefore 1.875 times greater than the actual decline time derived from the superposition time, or t_{Dda}=5.625 $\times$ 10^{-2}. At an apparent decline time of 5.625 $\times$ 10^{-2}, the dimensionless decline flow rate and flow rate integral values for a fracture with a dimensionless conductivity of 100 are equal to 0.73 and 1.3, respectively. This represents a difference in the decline time function of 87.5%, a difference in the decline flow rate value of approximately 24%, and a difference in the flow rate integral function of approximately 27%.

Nomenclature

a	=	intercept of relative permeability curve
A	=	drainage area of a well, ft^2 (m^2)
A_D	=	dimensionless drainage area, $A_D = A/L_c^{\,2}$
b	=	Arps analysis decline-curve exponent
b_f	=	fracture width, ft (m)
B	=	liquid formation volume factor, RB/STB (rcm/scm)
B_o	=	oil formation volume factor, RB/STB (rcm/scm)
B_{oi}	=	initial oil formation volume factor, RB/STB (rcm/scm)
B_w	=	water formation volume factor, RB/STB (rcm/scm)
B_g	=	gas formation volume factor, RB/scf (rcm/scm)
c	=	y-intercept outcome variable (from Eq. 7.10)
c_f	=	formation pore compressibility, 1/psia (1/Pa)
C	=	constant
C_{fD}	=	dimensionless fracture conductivity
c_g	=	gas compressibility, 1/psia (1/Pa)
c_o	=	oil compressibility, 1/psia (1/Pa)
c_t	=	total system compressibility, 1/psia (1/Pa)
$\bar{c}_t$	=	average total system compressibility, 1/psia (1/Pa)
c_w	=	water compressibility, 1/psia (1/Pa)
d	=	constant percentage decline rate, /unit of time
d_d	=	decline rate, 1/day
d_m	=	decline rate, 1/month
d_y	=	decline rate, 1/year
D	=	continuous decline rate, /unit of time
D_i	=	initial decline rate, 1/unit of time
E_R	=	fractional displacement efficiency, fraction
f_w	=	fractional flow term
G_p	=	cumulative gas produced, MMscf (scm)
h	=	reservoir net pay thickness, ft (m)
I_0	=	modified Bessel function of first kind of order zero
I_1	=	modified Bessel function of first kind of order one
k	=	average effective permeability, md (m^2)
k_a	=	absolute permeability, md (m^2)
k_f	=	fracture permeability, md (m^2)
k_g	=	effective permeability to gas, md (m^2)
k_o	=	effective permeability to oil, md (m^2)

k_{rg} = relative permeability to gas

k_{ro} = relative permeability to oil

k_w = effective permeability to water, md (m^2)

K_0 = modified Bessel function of second kind of order zero

K_1 = modified Bessel function of second kind of order one

L_c = system characteristic length, ft (m)

L_D = dimensionless effective wellbore length, $L_D = L_h/2h$

L_h = effective horizontal well length in pay zone, ft (m)

m = slope of permeability ratio k_o/k_w vs. N_p plot, 1/STB (1/scm)

n = slope of X plot straight line, 1/STB (1/scm)

N_p = cumulative oil produced, STB (scm)

N_{pi} = original oil in place, STB (scm)

p = pressure, psia (Pa)

p_0 = base pressure, lower limit of integration, psia (Pa)

p_i = initial reservoir pore pressure, psia (Pa)

$p_p(p)$ = real gas pseudopressure, psia^2/cp (Pa/s) $P_p(p) = 2\int_{p_0}^{p} \dfrac{p'dp'}{\mu_g z}$

$\tilde{P}_{wD}$ = Laplace space dimensionless wellbore pressure solution

p_{wD} = dimensionless wellbore pressure

p_{wf} = sandface flowing pressure, psia (Pa)

P_{Db} = rectangular reservoir imaging component for horizontal well

P_{Db1} = rectangular reservoir imaging component for horizontal well

P_{Db2} = rectangular reservoir imaging component for horizontal well

P_{Db3} = rectangular reservoir imaging component for horizontal well

q = flow rate, STB or Mscf/unit of time (scm/s)

q_1 = initial flow rate, STB or Mscf/unit of time (scm/s)

q_2 = second or current flow rate, STB or Mscf/unit of time (scm/s)

q_{avg} = average well flow rate, STB or Mscf/unit of time (scm/s)

q_{Dd} = dimensionless decline flow rate function

q_{Ddi} = dimensionless decline flow rate integral function

q_{Ddid} = dimensionless decline flow rate integral derivative function

$q_{Dext\infty}$ = dimensionless boundary flux

q_g = gas flow rate, Mscf/unit of time (scm/s)

q_i = initial flow rate, STB or Mscf/unit of time (scm/s)

$q_{i(max)}$ = theoretical maximum production rate, STB or Mscf/unit of time (scm/s)

q_n = nth production rate pointing the production history

q_o = oil flow rate, STB/unit of time (scm/s)

q_t = total well flow rate (all fluids), STB or Mscf/unit of time (scm/s)

q_w = water flow rate, STB/unit of time (scm/s)

q_{wD} = dimensionless wellbore flow rate

$\tilde{q}_{wD}$ = Laplace space dimensionless wellbore flow rate solution

$\tilde{q}_{Dext}$ = Laplace space dimensionless boundary flux

Q_p = cumulative production, STB or Mscf (scm)

Q_{pD} = dimensionless cumulative production

Q_{pDd} = dimensionless decline cumulative production function

$Q_{p\max}$ = theoretical maximum cumulative production, STB or Mscf (scm)

r_D = dimensionless radius, $r_D=r/L_c=r/r_w$

r_e = effective reservoir drainage radius, ft (m)

r_{eD} = dimensionless effective drainage radius, $r_{eD}=r_e/L_c$

r_w = wellbore radius, ft (m)

r_{wa} = apparent or effective wellbore radius, ft (m)

r_{wD} = dimensionless wellbore radius, $r_{wD}=r_{w/h}$

R = loss ratio, units of time (s)

R/P = reserves to production ratio, units of time (s)

R_s = solution GOR, scf/STB (scm/scm)

s = Laplace space parameter

S = steady-state skin effect

S_g = reservoir gas saturation, fraction of pore volume

S_o = reservoir oil saturation, fraction of pore volume

S_{or} = residual oil saturation, % of pore volume

S_w = water saturation, fraction or % of pore volume

S_{wi} = initial water saturation, fraction or % of pore volume

S_{wirr} = irreducible water saturation, % of pore volume

t = time, hours, days, months, years (s)

t' = time value parameter of integration

$\tilde{t}_D$ = dimensionless time relationship for a system with multiphase flow

t_D = dimensionless time, referenced to L_c

t_{DA} = dimensionless time, referenced to drainage area, A

t_{Dd} = dimensionless decline time function

t_{Dmb} = dimensionless material balance time function

t_{Dstart} = start dimensionless time at which the boundary flux becomes active

t_e = equivalent superposition time function value, day (s)

t_{mb} = material balance time function, day (s)

t_{pss} = time to reach pseudosteady-state or boundary-dominated flow, units of time (s)

t_{pssD} = dimensionless time to reach pseudosteady-state or boundary-dominated flow

T = average prevailing reservoir temperature, °R

u = parameter of integration

V_p = reservoir pore volume, acre-ft or RB (rcm)

W_i = cumulative volume of water injected, STB (scm)

W_p = cumulative water produced, STB (scm)

X = X direction spatial position, ft (m)

X_D = X direction dimensionless spatial position, $X_D=X/L_c$

X_D^* = equivalent fracture spatial position at which to evaluate the uniform flux fracture solution to obtain the finite-conductivity vertical fracture response

X_e = X direction drainage areal extent, ft (m)

X_{eD} = dimensionless X direction drainage areal extent, $X_{eD}=X_e/L_c$

X_f = effective fracture half-length, ft (m)

X_w = X direction wellbore spatial position, ft (m)

X_{wD} = dimensionless X direction wellbore spatial position, $X_{wD}=X_w/L_c$

Y = Y direction spatial position, ft (m)

Y_D = dimensionless Y direction spatial position, $Y_D=Y/L_c$

Y_e = Y direction drainage areal extent, ft (m)

Y_{eD} = dimensionless Y direction drainage areal extent, $Y_{eD}=Y_e/L_c$

Y_w = Y direction wellbore spatial position, ft (m)

Y_{wD} = dimensionless Y direction wellbore spatial position, $Y_{wD}=Y_w/L_c$

z = gas law deviation (supercompressibility) factor

$\bar{z}$ = average gas law deviation (supercompressibility) factor

Z = Z direction (vertical) spatial position, ft (m)

Z_D = dimensionless Z direction (vertical) spatial position, $Z_D=Z/h$

Z_w = Z direction (vertical) wellbore position, ft (m)

Z_{wD} = dimensionless Z direction (vertical) wellbore spatial position, $Z_{wD}=Z_w/h$

α = correction factor for material balance time function

Δp = pressure differential, psia (Pa) $\Delta p=p_i-p_{wf}$

Δq = difference in well flow rate, STB or Mscf/unit of time (scm/s)

Δt = difference in time, units of time (s)

δ = pseudoskin component caused by bounded nature of reservoir

ϕ = reservoir average effective porosity, fraction of bulk volume

$\bar{\lambda}_t$ = average total system mobility function, 1/cp (1/Pa·s)

μ = reservoir fluid viscosity, cp (Pa·s)

μ_g = gas viscosity, cp (Pa·s)

$\bar{\mu}_g$ = average gas viscosity, cp (Pa·s)

μ_{gi} = initial gas viscosity, cp (Pa·s)

μ_o = oil viscosity, cp (Pa·s)

μ_{oi} = initial oil viscosity, cp (Pa·s)

μ_w = water viscosity, cp (Pa·s)

σ = pseudoskin component caused by finite-conductivity vertical fracture

τ = parameter of integration

ξ = system imaging function caused by well completion and reservoir properties

ξ_a = adjusted system-imaging function (graphical scaling parameter)

ξ_f = system imaging function for a vertically fractured well in a closed rectangularly bounded reservoir

Functions

cos   = cosine function

cosh   = hyperbolic cosine

e   = exponential function

exp   = exponential function

ln   = natural logarithm

sin   = sine function

sinh   = hyperbolic sine

References

Agarwal, R.G., Gardner, D.C., Kleinstieber, S.W., and Fussell, D.D. 1999. Analyzing Well Production Data Using Combined Type Curve and Decline Curve Analysis Concepts. *SPEREE* **2** (5): 478–486. SPE-57916-PA. DOI: 10.2118/57916-PA.

Allen, R.E. 1931. Control of California Oil Curtailment. *Trans.*, AIME **149**: 47–66.

Arnold, R. and Anderson, R. 1908. Preliminary Report on the Coalinga Oil District. *US Geological Survey Bulletin 357,* 79.

Arps, J.J. 1945. Analysis of Decline Curves. *Trans.*, AIME **160**: 228–247.

Arps, J.J. 1956. Estimation of Primary Oil Reserves. *Trans.*, AIME **207**: 182–191.

Brons, F. 1963. On the Use and Misuse of Production Decline Curves. *The Producers Monthly* (September) 22–25.

Buckley, S.E. and Leverett, M.C. 1942. Mechanism of Fluid Displacement in Sands. *Trans.*, AIME **146**: 107–116.

Camacho-Velazquez, R.G. 1987. Well Performance Under Solution Gas Drive. PhD dissertation, University of Tulsa.

Camacho-Velazquez, R.G. and Raghavan, R. 1989. Boundary-Dominated Flow in Solution-Gas-Drive Reservoirs. *SPERE* **4** (4): 503–512. SPE-18562-PA. DOI: 10.2118/18562-PA.

Campbell, J.M. 1959. *Oil Property Evaluation*, 523. Englewood Cliffs, New Jersey: Prentice-Hall.

Campbell, J.M. 1959. *Analysis of Production-Performance Graphs,* 523. Englewood Cliffs, New Jersey: Prentice-Hall.

Carter, R.D. 1985. Type Curves for Finite Radial and Linear Gas-Flow Systems: Constant-Terminal-Pressure Case. *SPEJ* **25** (5): 719–728. SPE-12917-PA. DOI: 10.2118/12917-PA.

City of Long Beach. 1964. The Method for Establishing Recovery Factors for the Long Beach Unit. Equity Sub-Committee, Long Beach Unit (23 September).

Cox, D.O. 1978. Reservoir Limit Testing Using Production Data. *The Log Analyst* (March–April).

Craft, B.C. and Hawkins, M.F. 1959. *Applied Petroleum Reservoir Engineering*, 224. New York City: Prentice-Hall.

Crafton, J.W. 1997. Oil and Gas Well Evaluation Using the Reciprocal Productivity Index Method. Paper SPE 37409 presented at the SPE Production Operations Symposium, Oklahoma City, Oklahoma, 9–11 March. DOI: 10.2118/37409-MS.

Cutler, W.W. Jr. 1924. Estimation of Underground Oil Reserves by Well Production Curves. *US Geological Survey Bulletin 228,* 114.

Day, D.T. 1909. The Petroleum Resources of the United States. *US Geological Survey Bulletin 394* (Papers on the Conservation of Mineral Resources, National Conservation Commission) 30.

Doublet, L.E. and Blasingame, T.A. 1995a. Evaluation of Injection Well Performance Using Decline Type Curves. Paper SPE 35205 presented at the SPE Permian Basin Oil and Gas Recovery Conference, Midland, Texas, 27–29 March.

Doublet, L.E. and Blasingame, T.A. 1995b. Decline Curve Analysis Using Type Curves: Water Influx/Waterflood Cases. Paper SPE 30774 presented at the SPE Annual Technical Conference and Exhibition, Dallas, 22–25 October.

Doublet, L.E., Pande, P.K., McCollum, T.J., and Blasingame, T.A. 1994. Decline Curve Analysis Using Type Curves—Analysis of Oil Well Production Data Using Material Balance Time: Application to Field Cases.

Paper SPE 28688 presented at the SPE International Petroleum Conference and Exhibition of Mexico, Veracruz, Mexico, 10–13 October. DOI: 10.2118/28688-MS.

Earlougher, R.C. Jr. 1977. *Advances in Well Test Analysis*. Monograph Series, SPE, Richardson, Texas, **5.**

Ershaghi, I. and Omorigie, O. 1978. A Method for Extrapolation of Cut vs. Recovery Curves. *JPT* **30** (2): 203–204. SPE-6977-PA. DOI: 10.2118/6977-PA.

Ershaghi, I. and Abdassah, D. 1984. A Prediction Technique for Immiscible Processes Using Field Performance Data. *JPT* **36** (4): 664–670. SPE-10068-PA. DOI: 10.2118/10068-PA.

Ershaghi, I., Handy, L.L., and Hamdi, M. 1987. Application of the x-Plot Technique to the Study of Water Influx in the Sidi El-Itayem Reservoir, Tunisia. *JPT* **39** (9): 1129–1136. SPE-14209-PA. DOI: 10.2118/14209-PA.

Ferris, J., Knoles, D.B., Brown, R.H., and Stallman, R.W. 1962. Theory of Aquifer Tests. US Geological Survey, Water Supply Paper 1536E, 109.

Fetkovich, M.D., Guerrero, E.T., Fetkovich, M.J., and Thomas, L.K. 1986. Oil and Gas Relative Permeabilities Determined From Rate-Time Performance Data. Paper SPE 15431 presented at the SPE Annual Technical Conference and Exhibition, New Orleans, 5–8 October. DOI: 10.2118/15431-MS.

Fetkovich, M.J. 1971. A Simplified Approach to Water Influx Calculations—Finite Aquifer Systems. *JPT* **23** (7): 814–828. SPE-2603-PA. DOI: 10.2118/2603-PA.

Fetkovich, M.J. 1980. Decline Curve Analysis Using Type Curves. *JPT* **32** (6): 1065–1077. SPE-4629-PA. DOI: 10.2118/4629-PA.

Fetkovich, M.J. and Thrasher, T.S. 1979. Constant Well Pressure Testing and Analysis in Low Permeability Reservoirs. Paper SPE 7928 presented at the SPE/DOE Symposium on Low Permeability Gas Reservoirs, Denver. DOI: 10.2118/7928-MS.

Fetkovich, M.J., Fetkovich, E.J., and Fetkovich, M.D. 1996. Useful Concepts for Decline Curve Forecasting, Reserve Estimation, and Analysis. *SPERE* **11** (1): 13–22. SPE-28628-PA. DOI: 10.2118/28628-PA.

Fetkovich, M.J., Vienot, M.E., Bradley, M.D., and Kiesow, U.G. 1987. Decline Curve Analysis Using Type Curves: Case Histories. *SPEFE* **2** (4): 637–656. SPE-13169-PA. DOI: 10.2118/13169-PA.

Gentry, R.W. and McCray, A.W. 1978. The Effect of Reservoir and Fluid Properties on Production Decline Curves. *JPT* **30** (9): 1327–1341. SPE-18562-PA. DOI: 10.2118/18562-PA.

Gringarten, A.C., Ramey, H.J. Jr., and Raghavan, R. 1974. Unsteady-State Pressure Distributions Created by a Well With a Single Infinite-Conductivity Vertical Fracture. *SPEJ* **14** (4): 347–360. SPE-4051-PA. DOI: 10.2118/4051-PA.

Horner, D.R. 1951. Pressure Build-up in Wells, *Proc.*, Third World Petroleum Congress, The Hague, II: 503.

Huddleston, B.P. 1991. Class Notes, Texas A&M University, College Station, Texas.

Jacob, C.E. and Lohman, S.W. 1952. Nonsteady Flow to a Well of Constant Drawdown in an Extensive Aquifer. *Trans.*, AGU (August): 559–569.

Johnson, R.H. and Bollens, A.L. 1927. The Loss-Ratio Method of Extrapolating Oil Well Decline Curves. *Trans.*, AIME **27:** 771.

Kelkar, B.G. and Perez, G. 1988. Discussion of a New Approach to the Hyperbolic Curve. *JPT* **40** (12): 1617–1619. SPE-18728-PA. DOI: 10.2118/18728-PA.

Lee, W.J., Harrell, R.R., and McCain, W.D. Jr. 1972. Evaluation of a Gas Well Testing Method. Paper SPE 3872 presented at the SPE Natural Gas Technology Symposium, Omaha, Nebraska, 18–19 May.

Lewis, J.O. and Beal, C.H. 1918. Some New Methods for Estimating the Future Production of Oil Wells. *Trans.*, AIME **59:** 492.

Lijek, S.J. 1989. Simple Performance Plots Used in Rate-Time Determination and Waterflood Analysis. Paper SPE 19847 presented at the SPE Annual Technical Conference and Exhibition, San Antonio, Texas, 8–11 October. DOI: 10.2118/19847-MS.

Lo, K.K., Warner, H.R. Jr., and Johnson, J.B. 1990. A Study of the Post-Breakthrough Characteristics of Waterfloods. Paper SPE 20064 presented at the SPE California Regional Meeting, Ventura, California, 4–6 April. DOI: 10.2118/20064-MS.

Long, D.R. and Davis, M.J. 1988. A New Approach to the Hyperbolic Curve. *JPT* **40** (7): 909–912. SPE-16237-PA.

Marsh, H.N. 1928. Method of Appraising Results of Production Control of Oil Well. *API and Prod. Eng. Bull. 202*, 66.

McCray, T.L. 1990. Reservoir Analysis Using Production Data and Adjusted Time. MS thesis, Texas A&M University, College Station, Texas.

Muskat, M. 1949. *Physical Principles of Oil Production,* 458. New York City: McGraw-Hill Book Company.

Nind, T.E.W. 1981. *Principles of Oil Well Production,* second edition. New York City: McGraw-Hill Book Company.

Occurrence of Oil and Gas in Northeast Texas. 1989. P.W. Shoemaker, ed., East Texas Geological Society, Tyler, Texas.

Ozkan, E. 1988. Performance of Horizontal Wells. PhD dissertation, University of Tulsa.

Palacio, J.C. and Blasingame, T.A. 1993. Decline-Curve Analysis Using Type Curves—Analysis of Gas Well Production Data. Paper SPE 25909 presented at the SPE Rocky Mountain Regional/Low Permeability Reservoirs Symposium, Denver, 12–14 April. DOI: 10.2118/25909-MS.

Pirson, S.J. 1935. Production Decline Curve of Oil Well May be Extrapolated by Loss Ratio. *Oil & Gas J.* (14 November) **26:** 34–35.

Poe, B.D. Jr. 2002. Effective Well and Reservoir Evaluation Without the Need for Well Pressure History. Paper SPE 77691 presented at the SPE Annual Technical Conference and Exhibition, San Antonio, Texas, 29 September–2 October. DOI: 10.2118/77691-MS.

Poe, B.D. Jr. 2003. Production Diagnostic Analyses With Incomplete or No Pressure Records. Paper SPE 84224 presented at the SPE Annual Technical Conference and Exhibition, Denver, 5–8 October. DOI: 10.2118/84224-MS.

Poe, B.D. Jr. 2005. Method and Apparatus For Effective Well and Reservoir Evaluation Without the Need for Well Pressure History. US Patent 6,842,700.

Poe, B.D. Jr. and Marhaendrajana, T. 2002. Investigation of the Relationship Between the Dimensionless and Dimensional Analytic Transient Well Performance Solutions in Low-Permeability Gas Reservoirs. Paper SPE 77467 presented at the SPE Annual Technical Conference and Exhibition, San Antonio, Texas, 29 September–2 October. DOI: 10.2118/77467-MS.

Prats, M., Matthews, C.S., Jewett, R.L., and Baker, J.D. 1959. Prediction of Injection Rate and Production History for Multifluid Five-Spot Floods. *Trans.*, AIME **216:** 98–105.

Purvis, R.A. 1985. Analysis of Production-Performance Graphs. *J. Cdn. Pet. Tech.* (July–August) 44. Paper 85-04-03.

Purvis, R.A. 1987. Further Analysis of Production-Performance Graphs. *J. Cdn. Pet. Tech.* (July–August) 74. Paper 87-04-07.

Ramey, H.J. Jr. and Cobb, W.M. 1971. A General Buildup Theory for a Well in a Closed Drainage Area. *JPT* **23** (12): 1493–1505. SPE-3012-PA. DOI: 10.2118/3012-PA.

Shih, M.Y. and Blasingame, T.A. 1995. Decline Curve Analysis Using Type Curves: Horizontal Wells. Paper SPE 29572 presented at the SPE Joint Rocky Mountain Regional/Low Permeability Reservoirs Symposium, Denver, 19–22 March.

Slider, H.C. 1968. A Simplified Method of Hyperbolic Decline Curve Analysis. *JPT* **20** (3): 235–236. SPE-1936-PA. DOI: 10.2118/1936-PA.

Snyder, R.W. and Ramey, H.J. Jr. 1967. Application of Buckley-Leverett Displacement Theory to Noncommunicating Layered Systems. *JPT* **19** (11): 1500–1506. SPE-1645-PA. DOI: 10.2118/1645-PA.

Spivey, J.P., Gatens, J.M., Semmelbeck, M.E., and Lee, W.J. 1992. Integral Type Curves for Advanced Decline Curve Analysis. Paper SPE 24301 presented at the SPE Mid-Continent Gas Symposium, Amarillo, Texas, 13–14 April. DOI: 10.2118/24301-MS.

Stehfest, H. 1970. Numerical Inversion of Laplace Transforms (Algorithm 368 with correction). *Communications of the ACM* **13** (1): 47–49.

Timmerman, E.H. 1971. Predict Performance of Water Floods Graphically. *Petroleum Engineer* (November).

Tsarevich, K.A. and Kuranov, I.F. 1966. Calculation of the Flow Rates for the Center Well in a Circular Reservoir Under Elastic Conditions. *Problems of Reservoir Hydrodynamics*, Part 1, 9–34. Leningrad, USSR.

van Everdingen, A.F. and Hurst, W. 1949. Application of the Laplace Transformation to Flow Problems in Reservoirs. *Trans.*, AIME **186:** 305–324.

Vance, H. 1961. *History of Petroleum Engineering*, 1039. API, Boyd Publishing Company.

Welge, H.J. 1952. A Simplified Method for Computing Oil Recovery by Gas or Water Drive. *Trans.*, AIME **195:** 91–98.

Winestock, A.G. and Colpitts, G.P. 1965. Advances in Estimating Gas Well Deliverability, *J. Cdn. Pet. Tech.* **4** (3): 111–119.

AUTHOR INDEX

SUBJECT INDEX